THE NATURAL HEDGEHOG

Frontispiece
*Pip, a healthy young hedgehog born at the WHH and
Crystal's brother, forages in a native oak woodland.*

THE
NATURAL
HEDGEHOG

LENNI SYKES
WITH
JANE DURRANT

FOREWORD BY
VIRGINIA McKENNA
Founder of "The Born Free Foundation"

Gaia Books Limited

A GAIA ORIGINAL
Conceived by Lenni Sykes in collaboration with Jane Durrant

Lenni Sykes LCH ACOH is an experienced homeopath and healer with a background in veterinary nursing. Her lifelong love of animals has led her to specialise in working with wildlife. She has worked with various wildlife hospitals, including New Quay Bird and Wildlife Hospital, the Welsh Hedgehog Hospital and the RSPCA's Wildlife Hospital in Somerset, advising on how best to use homeopathy on their charges. Lenni has written many articles and lectured extensively on homeopathy and her work with wildlife.

Jane Durrant founded the Welsh Hedgehog Hospital in 1986. As honorary member of the British Hedgehog Preservation Society she is renowned for her research into hedgehog illness and her commitment to finding safe ways to treat them. Jane and her hospital have attracted much media attention, including features on national and international TV and radio. One newspaper referred to Jane as "the hedgehogs' own Florence Nightingale". Dedicated to saving hedgehogs, she also works as a professional book illustrator.

Editor	Pip Morgan
Designer	Patrick Nugent
Illustrator	Jane Durrant
Photographer	Alan Durrant
Production	Susan Walby

DEDICATION

This book is dedicated to Gaia, the living being that supports us all, to Artemis, and to hedgehogs everywhere.

ACKNOWLEDGEMENTS

To all those who offered support, encouragement, suggestions, and help – thank you, it is all appreciated. In particular, I would like to thank: Jane Durrant for her dedication and determination to help hedgehogs. Without her work there would have been little to fill the pages of this book. All at Gaia for their hard work, especially Pip and Patrick. Our agent Frances Kelly. Jean and Alan Bryant of New Quay Bird Hospital. Chris Aukland, homeopathic vet, for checking the text for veterinary blunders. Virginia McKenna, Nigel Reeve (his excellent book "Hedgehogs" has been an invaluable source of reference), Dick Best of the British Wildlife Rehabilitation Council, and Christopher Day. The British Hedgehog Preservation Society for their help and support. Tim Thomas, Head of RSPCA Wildlife Unit. Colin Seddon and Sandra Harvey of the RSPCA's Wildlife Hospital in West Hatch, Somerset, and their vet Paul Yates for providing case histories. Harry Oldfield for taking P.I.P scans. Kay Heaton-Jones of the Hedgehog Helpline. Colin Orr, manager of Waterstones, Stratford. Mary Jane and Chris Hopes, Jackie Carey and Niels Eiriksson for their fax machines. Writing this book whilst recovering from two accidents would not have been possible without Sarah Wallace, my cranial osteopath, whose skill achieved what all the King's horses and all the King's men couldn't have done! All those who've sent me healing, especially Keith Casburn. Everyone at the sadly demised Only Natural café, which became my second home and main source of sustenance. Margaret Seager for her years of support and for being willing to locum at a moment's notice, so I could do things with hedgehogs, dolphins and other wildlife, knowing that my practice was in good hands. All my friends for their support, in particular Catherine Wuidart, Mary Jane Hopes, Julie Campbell, Amanda Root, Jerome Flynn, and my mother Margaret Sykes. Last but not least, thanks to Tarquin.

Jane Durrant personally wishes to thank all those who have helped with or supported the WHH over the years, and of course the staff – the WHH couldn't have survived without you. On behalf of the WHH and staff, I would like to thank: Pedigree Pet Foods; The British Hedgehog Preservation Society; the WHH's vets – Mr. W.J.Downes of Aberystwyth, Mr. E.Jones and all the vets at the Priory Practice, Cardigan; the Veterinary Investigation Centre, Aberystwyth; The Harry Edwards Spiritual Healing Sanctuary; Winfalcon's Healing Centre; Harry Oldfield; Christopher Day (for his help with Whitie); Dru Burdon of the Jersey Hedgehog Group; Matt James of Bayer Diagnostics; David Bartram of Janssen Animal Health; Jon Morgan of Volac International Ltd.

Contents

Foreword

If, as I did, you grew up with Beatrix Potter's Mrs Tiggywinkle, you will already have an abiding affection for hedgehogs. Such affection is not usually accompanied by any real understanding of this fascinating animal. But, after reading *The Natural Hedgehog*, all Mrs Tiggywinkle fans, as well as readers "meeting" hedgehogs for the first time, will be enriched and enlightened as they reach the final page.

Animals have a tough life nowadays – threatened, it would seem, on all sides. And it appears to make no difference if, as hedgehogs were, you were once worshipped as a god and revered as a religious symbol. One only has to look at elephants to realise that, for an animal, such status affords no real protection.

Essentially, this book is about looking after injured, sick or orphaned hedgehogs – but in a very special way. A natural way. Lenni's homeopathic treatment and alternative remedies are remarkable for their detail and comprehensiveness. I read with growing admiration for this holistic approach to animal care. It is this approach and the appraisal of the importance of the **individual** animal that made this book so attractive to me. That and Jane's delicate and delightful pictures that simply and vividly bring to life the character and personality of the hedgehog and the environment in which it tries to survive.

Hedgehogs are fortunate indeed to have such a champion. The healing skills and painstaking care Jane bestows on each patient in her Welsh Hedgehog Hospital reveal to us a person of sensitivity and compassion. I have been informed, fascinated and delighted by this book and, if I now see a hedgehog in my garden, I will see much more than a "Mrs Tiggywinkle", but my affection will be undiminished.

VIRGINIA MCKENNA *June 1995*

European hedgehogs may vary in colour from one individual to another. Here you can see typical variations, from white to blonde and from normal to black. All these hedgehogs come from Wales, except the blonde, which comes from a colony on Alderney in the Channel Islands.

Sootie is an albino, with red eyes, pink skin, and pure white spines and hair.

Whitie is more unusual than an albino because he has black eyes to go with his pink skin and pure white spines and hair. His offspring, which were brown, were released into the wild.

This blonde hedgehog shows more pigment, and is probably much stronger, than an albino.

Spottie is a pale golden hedgehog which, at birth, had no tail and brown freckles on his pink skin.

Woollie shows the usual colouration of hedgehogs. Pink noses and white patches or spines are common.

Blackie has dark spines and hairs, a colouration that seems to be even rarer than white.

Introduction

Hedgehogs play an important part in the natural and cultural heritage of many countries. Everyone knows them, everyone – or almost everyone – loves them. Their extinction as a species would mean losing a valuable part of our history. Their very familiarity deceives us into taking their continued survival for granted. Yet they are under threat, not from predators, but from an assortment of manmade problems, against which they have little or no defence.

Hedgehogs belong to an ancient family. They have survived because of their great ability to adapt to changing circumstances and because they have few natural enemies. But will the threat of modern civilization prove too much for them or can they adapt quickly enough to survive it? It would be a great pity if such a hardy and ever-popular creature, so well equipped to deal with most natural threats, is lost to future generations at our hands. Hedgehogs fill an important niche in the ecosystem and are valuable friends to farmers and gardeners because of their role in keeping populations of insects and molluscs in check.

Pollution is one major threat, just as it is to all wildlife. Humans continually release a wide range of often lethal chemicals into the environment. When combined with other chemicals they can produce noxious cocktails that are even more hazardous. Whilst hedgehogs are not susceptible or at least highly resistant to many natural poisons, they are vulnerable to many chemicals (such as the metaldehyde in slug pellets) commonly applied to agricultural and urban land.

Another major threat is habitat destruction. As its name implies, the hedgehog likes to live in areas where hedges provide cover. Modern agricultural practice has led to the wholesale removal of hedgerows in order to make larger fields, which are said to be easier and more cost-effective to cultivate. In addition, the construction of more and more roads, housing estates, car parks and out-of-town shopping centres continually encroaches on the countryside and its wild inhabitants.

Mechanization may have helped our own species, but it has proved deadly to the hedgehog, with motor vehicles and strimmers competing for the highest number of casualties. For many people, their first sighting of a wild hedgehog is one squashed on the road. Such losses have wider implications than just the death of individuals, since many are adult females which are either pregnant or nursing young which will have no chance of surviving alone.

Hedgehogs injured by motor vehicles and strimmers, as well as hedgehogs that are sick from other causes, often find their way into the hands of a concerned person who then has the task of caring for the animal until it is well enough to be returned to the wild. This book is written for such people, regardless of their experience, or lack of it.

Rescuing and rehabilitating wildlife is a controversial issue. Are we interfering with the natural balance by taking in sick and injured animals? One such animal saved could mean a predator going hungry, having lost the opportunity to catch what would have been easy prey. By intervening, are we playing God, and, if we are, do we have the right to do so? Does the end justify the means? Inevitably, it will be enormously stressful for any wild creature to be taken out of its natural habitat and handled by people. And after all our efforts, what chance do such animals have of surviving back in the wild after a period in our care?

In answer to this last question, research has shown that such animals can thrive, provided they are fit enough when released. As far as the "natural balance" is concerned, is there truly such a thing any more, considering the changes we have already wrought on an unsuspecting environment? For further expansion of this theme, I refer the reader to Bill McKibben's excellent but alarming book *The End Of Nature*.

Since it is clear that mankind's development has itself been responsible for causing the majority of the problems now threatening the planet's wildlife, it seems only right that we should take responsibility for this and do what we can to help provide solutions for the problems we have created. This is not playing God, it is simply a question of attempting to make amends. This is best achieved on a large scale by

GENUS ATELERIX

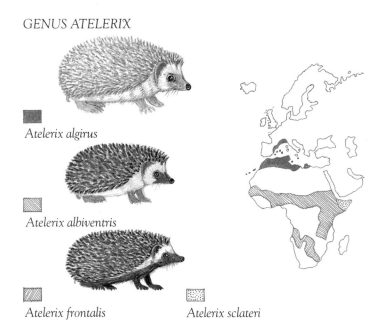

Hedgehogs are distant relatives of shrews, moles, tenrecs, and moonrats. All these animals belong to the order Insectivora of the subdivision Liptophyla. Hedgehogs belong to the family Erinaceidae, which is made up of spiny hedgehogs and hairy hedgehogs. As these pages show, there are 14 species of spiny hedgehog distributed throughout much of the world (see p.19). The European hedgehog, Erinaceus europaeus, is found throughout Europe and in New Zealand, where it was introduced in the last century. The species Atelerix albiventris has been imported into the United States, where it is kept only in captivity.

Atelerix algirus

Atelerix albiventris

Atelerix frontalis

Atelerix sclateri

GENUS ERINACEUS

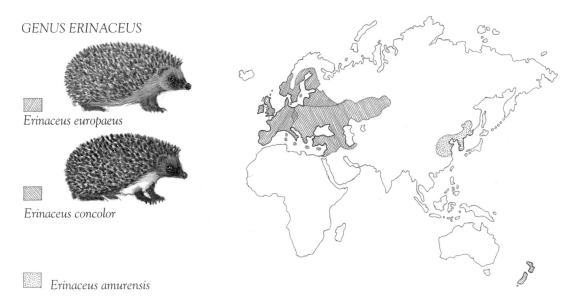

Erinaceus europaeus

Erinaceus concolor

Erinaceus amurensis

GENUS PARAECHINUS

 Paraechinus aethiopicus

Paraechinus hypomelas

Paraechinus micropus

GENUS HEMIECHINUS

Hemiechinus auritus

Hemiechinus collaris

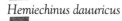 *Hemiechinus dauuricus*

Hemiechinus hughi

11

protecting wildlife and the environment, but there is also a case for helping individual animals to survive.

This book is called *The Natural Hedgehog* because of its emphasis on treating hedgehogs naturally. By providing medicinal help and general care that is natural, safe and holistic, you will be able to achieve two important aims. First, you will avoid adding toxins and side-effects to a sick animal's problems; and second, you will provide conditions that are as close to those experienced in the wild as possible, and so keep stress to a minimum.

This natural theme is also applied to the suggestions for helping the hedgehog as a species, by working to save the hedgehog's environment and reducing manmade perils. No species can be saved in isolation. In order to save the hedgehog it is vital to ensure that the entire ecosystem is sustained in balance. Although this needs to be achieved globally, by creating a sustainable and safe environment for wildlife in your own garden you will be making a vital contribution.

The question "Are hedgehogs necessary?" was recently put to me. My answer was that I believe every species has the right to its continued existence, regardless of whether we (as a species) find it useful or necessary. It would be impossible to determine the effect on the ecological balance if hedgehogs became extinct, since no species exists in a vacuum. I added that, in the case of hedgehogs, there is also reason to support them for our own ends. If we had set about purposefully creating a species to control those that are the greatest menace to our crops and garden plants, we couldn't have done better than create the hedgehog. For not only does it target the species which do most damage, it also tends to leave alone others (e.g. ladybirds) that are helpful to us.

The views expressed in this book are based on the experiences of hedgehogs brought into care at the Welsh Hedgehog Hospital (abbreviated throughout the book as WHH). The WHH was established in 1986. Its aims are to cure and rehabilitate sick, orphaned, and injured hedgehogs. The hospital has a particularly high success rate with its charges. This we attribute to the emphasis on natural care, using treatments which are safe and holistic and which reflect the hedgehog's natural lifestyle as closely as possible. This approach is combined with modern veterinary methods, including the use of sophisticated laboratory equipment to aid diagnosis. Whenever possible, hedgehogs are released back into their area of origin once they are well.

We hope that this book will add to the reader's knowledge of hedgehogs and their lives, whilst also acting as a guide to those caring for hedgehogs and as a useful reference book for anyone using homeopathy on animals. The text is supported by Jane's illustrations, drawn from her many years of practical experience in caring for hedgehogs.

The first chapter provides essential knowledge for anyone needing to judge how best to care for hedgehogs in captivity. It covers the history and natural history of hedgehogs (exploding some myths and showing how others are based on fact), and the hazards facing them. Chapter Two gives the reader a step-by-step guide on what to do with a sick or injured hedgehog, explaining how to assess its needs and providing detailed instruction on all aspects of hedgehog care, including housing, diet, nursing, feeding, and rehabilitation. It also shows how to encourage hedgehogs into your garden and make a safe environment for them.

The third chapter is devoted to homeopathy and its uses in helping hedgehogs, plus combatting parasites. Chapter Four introduces other complementary therapies that have been used successfully at the WHH. The Appendices contain Case Histories, a Repertory, and a Materia Medica. The Case Histories tell of hedgehogs treated homeopathically, revealing how the remedies work and, in some instances, how they compare with conventional drugs. The Repertory is an A to Z of symptoms and remedies. The Materia Medica contains details of the main homeopathic remedies you can use to treat hedgehogs.

Working under my guidance as its homeopath, the WHH has many years of experience using homeopathy on hedgehogs. The resulting material on homeopathic prescribing provides guidance suitable for complete beginners and those with expertise in this area. The advice on hedgehog care is both appealing and useful to people who would like to care for hedgehogs and to those who have already embarked upon this most rewarding of activities. Finally, much of the material is also relevant to the homeopathic treatment of other animals, since the basics of prescribing and the remedy uses are standard for all species.

CHAPTER ONE

Hedgehog Habits

The ancestors of hedgehogs lived in Asia some 25 million years ago. Their descendants spread to Europe, Africa, and North America, where the population has become extinct. Today's hedgehogs are either spiny or hairy. They belong to the family Erinaceidae, which has no close living relatives. This book focuses on spiny hedgehogs, of which there are 14 species, and in particular on the European hedgehog (*Erinaceus europaeus*). As its name implies, this species is found throughout Europe. In the 19th century, British settlers introduced it to New Zealand. More recently, an African hedgehog (*Atelerix albiventris*) has been imported into the United States under the guise of scientific work and sold in pet shops. Despite their individual differences, the information given on hedgehog care and treatment is appropriate for all species.

A glazed model of a hedgehog from Ancient Egypt, dated about 2000 BC.

Myths and Folklore

Hedgehogs have always attracted a fair amount of attention from humans, not all of it good. We have persecuted and killed them in their thousands; we have even put a price on their heads. Gamekeepers exterminated them in an effort to protect game birds' eggs and chicks. While hedgehogs sometimes eat eggs and chicks, it is doubtful whether they were responsible for sufficient losses to justify the sustained and extensive war against them.

Throughout human history, hedgehogs have been the subject of myths and folklore in many parts of the globe. Perhaps this is because of their curious appearance and apparently eccentric behaviour, which often lends itself to misunderstandings about their activities. Indeed, a

Crystal was born at the WHH and is seen here foraging amongst primroses in the hedgehog garden. She has an even mixture of white and brown spines.

14

great deal of hedgehog behaviour, such as self-anointing, is not fully understood. And then there are the famous stories, accounts of which are often confusing and contradictory, of hedgehogs carrying fruit or suckling on the udder of a cow.

Hedgehogs will eat fruit, but not as a mainstay of their diet. Since they do not store food, they are unlikely to collect fruit on purpose in order to eat it later. So what is the source of the tales and drawings, from areas of the globe populated by spiny hedgehogs, of these animals carrying fruit such as apples on their spines? If such drawings are to scale, the apples shown would have to be very small (such as crab apples) or the hedgehogs exceptionally large individuals. Grapes would more easily stick to a hedgehog's spines and many hedgehogs are partial to them. The most likely explanation is that the fruit, particularly if it is rotting or fairly soft, emits an aroma that stimulates a hedgehog to perform the act of self-anointment. When the hedgehog rolls on its back any fruit beneath it would accidentally become impaled and would remain there as the animal walks away (see p.18).

Tales of hedgehogs suckling cows' udders are far-fetched. They could not reach an udder unless the cow was lying down – and what cow would stay lying down in such circumstances? Besides, adult hedgehogs do not have the ability to suckle. Country hedgehogs will lap up milk that leaks from a cow's full udder or milk spilled on the dairy floor. Hedgehogs cannot digest cow's milk very well, though it may help them over a period when other food is scarce, provided they are eating other things and are free from intestinal worms or digestive problems.

One patient at the WHH was found orphaned in the dairy on a farm. He had collapsed in a pool of milk and was almost drowned. Only four weeks old and unable to fend for himself, he weighed only 30 grams. He had probably turned to the milk out of a desperate hunger. At first, he seemed unlikely to survive because his condition was so poor. But although it took him a long time to grow, he did recover eventually and was released back into the wild successfully. During the first year following his release, he returned regularly to the WHH and was apparently thriving.

Another common piece of folklore is that hedgehogs are immune to adder venom. Whilst they do possess a greater immunity to most

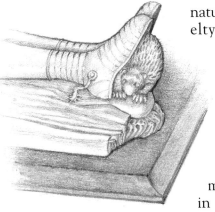

A stone heraldic hedgehog lies at the feet of the Kyle family memorial at Much Marcle in Herefordshire.

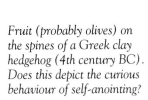

Fruit (probably olives) on the spines of a Greek clay hedgehog (4th century BC). Does this depict the curious behaviour of self-anointing?

natural poisons than other animals, scientific research (involving a cruelty we do not endorse) has shown that they are not completely immune to snake bites. Some die, though they tend to survive the poison much longer than other animals. When confronted with a striking snake, a hedgehog will rapidly curl up, its spines preventing the snake's teeth from reaching its flesh. In some circumstances, hedgehogs will attack and eat snakes, perhaps when other sources of food are scarce. They will also eat snakes' eggs, but are unlikely to break them open themselves.

Hedgehogs have been killed for food and for their reported medicinal benefits. Gypsies, for instance, are said to have baked them in clay to remove the spines. Their medicinal properties were once thought to relieve ailments such as eye complaints, boils, baldness, colic and even leprosy. (Hedgehogs, like humans, are susceptible to leprosy.)

Another piece of folklore is that hedgehogs can foretell a change of wind and then alter the entrances to their homes accordingly. Because of this, they have been used for weather divination. They are also a symbol for protection and self-preservation, not surprisingly with such an armoury of prickles. This may be why the hedgehog, or urcheon as it is also known, appears on a number of heraldic coats of arms.

Hedgehog worship formed part of various cultures, especially those worshipping the Earth Mother Goddess. It was believed that she would often take the form of a hedgehog. In particular, hedgehogs were associated with the Babylonian goddess Ishtar, the goddess of love and war, also known by her Greek name Astarte. Ishtar was associated with the planet Venus and identified with the Sumerian goddess Inanna and the Phoenician Ashtoreth. In Ancient Egypt, the hedgehog was revered as a symbol of reincarnation because of its death-like hibernation followed by rebirth in the spring.

Hedgehogs have appeared in numerous stories throughout the world. In Lewis Carroll's *Alice in Wonderland*, for instance, rolled-up hedgehogs were used as croquet balls – just as in real life these creatures are often the kicked and beaten victims of some cruel playground sport. And the hedgehog, not known for its cleanliness, was the unlikely choice for the washerwoman in Beatrix Potter's much-loved *The Tale of Mrs Tiggywinkle*.

17

Self-anointing

This curious feature of hedgehog behaviour has so far baffled experts as to its purpose – if, indeed, it has one. The hedgehog repeatedly licks an object or substance whilst producing a large quantity of frothy saliva. The hedgehog flicks the saliva over its spines with its long tongue, often contorting itself to reach every part of its spiny coat. This process may last anything from a few minutes to several hours. An animal will often go back over and over again to the same spot and repeat the procedure.

Some hedgehogs seem to self-anoint more than others. The stimulus to do it seems to be a strong odour (see p.16). A seemingly endless variety of substances can trigger the process; anything from the hedgehog's own feces or urine – or that of other animals – to foodstuffs, furniture, or footwear! By the time the hedgehog has finished anointing itself, it will obviously have acquired the odour of the trigger substance plus the odour of its own saliva. In an animal with such a strong sense of smell, this will clearly communicate something to other hedgehogs in the area. But what the message may be is unknown to us. If the substance is particularly noxious, it may also deter predators.

A 13th-century English manuscript shows hedgehogs with apples on their spines. Could this be due to self-anointing?

Living Wild

Hedgehogs thrive in a wide variety of climates and cover a large portion of the globe. One of the most widely distributed species is the European hedgehog, which is the main focus of this book. This species is found throughout Europe, wherever there are deciduous trees and bushes, and in New Zealand. The Algerian hedgehog is found in North Africa and southern parts of Spain and France. There are three species of African hedgehog found on that continent and also in the Middle East. The long-eared hedgehog also inhabits the Middle East and is found throughout Asia and Russia. Desert hedgehogs can be found from Morocco to India. The Chinese hedgehog is very similar to the European hedgehog and seems to inhabit similar terrain, though it is found only in China.

Hedgehogs in colder climates, where hibernation is necessary in order to survive the winter, need materials suitable for nest building. They usually use leaves of deciduous trees, which is perhaps why they are less common in areas where there are few trees or only conifers. Hedgehogs also inhabit hedgerows, burrows, and other shelters, including manmade shelters such as compost heaps and underneath sheds. They generally adapt very well to urban environments, finding gardens, parks, and golf courses suitable, although not always safe.

Town Hedgehogs, Country Hedgehogs

Several miles from the nearest town and a mile outside the nearest village, the WHH stands in one of the most sparsely populated and unpolluted regions of the UK. Most of the animals that have been brought to the WHH come from villages. The few exceptions are brought in from an urban environment (from cities and towns) and from the countryside. The former are referred to as "town" hedgehogs. Within these two categories lie a diversity of environmental circumstances. Hedgehogs from a city have to cope with a great deal more human activity and its effects than their village-dwelling cousins, yet both are considered to be town hedgehogs. Within the countryside, too, there are widely differing circumstances, especially with regard to terrain, weather conditions, food supply, predators, and human activity and influence.

Jane has observed a tendency in the local town hedgehog population to produce larger litter sizes, on average, than the local country hedgehogs. Some further research into this phenomenon would be valuable. Differences between the lives of town and country hedgehogs are certainly reflected in their quality of health.

Typically, town hedgehogs have a heavy parasite burden, including many fleas. By contrast, country hedgehogs are not prone to fleas or other parasites, except when sick or injured. Recently, Jane tested some fully grown country adults and found no parasites, either internally or externally. The New Zealand population is free from fleas because they were not introduced to the islands with the hedgehogs. In fact, the New Zealand hedgehogs are thriving: the warm climate means fewer hibernation casualties; predators are rare; and food is abundant, with little competition from other insectivores. However, the favourable conditions for hedgehogs in New Zealand have not prevented them from succumbing to mite infestation and ringworm.

Why is there a difference in parasite susceptibility between town and country hedgehogs? Possibly because country hedgehogs have a better quality diet, and suffer less pollution and less stress from human disturbance. These factors could contribute to a healthier immune system and a greater resistance to parasites. Town-dwelling hedgehogs may not be able to find enough natural sources of nourishment, and consequently have learned to scavenge from human discards. The natural food they do find is more likely to contain residues of pesticides and other chemicals than the same food found in the country.

Hazel shows her large, blunt incisors, which have a central gap on the top jaw. The lower incisors fit into this gap when her mouth is closed.

However, hedgehogs living in intensively farmed rural areas may not be that much better off than town hedgehogs with regard to human disturbance, pesticide residues, and other such problems. In fact, hedgehogs are rare if not altogether absent from arable areas. This is presumably due to loss of hedgerows for habitat, and loss of food supply due to the heavy use of pesticides. Country hedgehogs live in much larger territories than town hedgehogs, especially the males, which cover considerable distances. Reduced habitat and food supply could confine hedgehogs to a smaller area and so expose them to more concentrated hazards. More research is needed to determine whether environmental factors influence the health and parasite burdens of hedgehogs.

When a hedgehog has been rescued and is ready to go back into the wild, it must be released into a similar environment to the one from which it came. Country dwellers would be extremely bewildered to suddenly find themselves in an urban environment with its different smells and different sources of food and water. Town hedgehogs, too, would find a life in the country disorientating. A number of stories confirm this. For example, a mother and her litter of babies were rescued from a town after she was attacked by a dog. Shortly before they were to be released, one of the babies discovered how to open their cage and liberated the whole family! The mother obviously did not take to it and only stayed around the area for three weeks, long enough for her babies to mature. She was later identified in the nearby village, with a new litter of young. The closest she could find to her home environment was a group of buildings with nearby compost heaps, which make good nesting sites.

Hedgehog Diet

Hedgehogs are insectivores. Their diet consists largely of beetles, caterpillars, and earthworms. They also eat a wide variety of other insects such as millipedes and earwigs, the larvae of the crane-fly, slugs and snails. Woodlice, although abundant, do not seem particularly appealing to most hedgehog palates, although they will eat ground beetles and millipedes, both of which are distasteful to other animals. Hedgehogs have also been known to eat dead bees and to jump in the air to catch moths. Though there may be some dietary differences due to availability of prey, in general their diet is similar regardless of species or geographical location.

Whilst primarily dependent on an invertebrate diet, hedgehogs occasionally eat carrion, small mammals, and tiny nestlings on the ground. They sometimes eat birds' eggs and have made some enemies because of this – they have been accused of significantly lowering bird populations in some areas. In experiments conducted at the WHH, hedgehogs showed no interest in hen or quail eggs unless the eggs were

Life span
Hedgehogs in the wild commonly live for three or four years, though they may reach up to seven or eight years. In captivity in Germany, a hedgehog has lived to the grand old age of sixteen years, but this is exceptional – up to seven years is more normal. Life expectancy will obviously be very much affected by such factors as the presence of predators, abundance of prey species, climatic conditions, and the abundance of the motor vehicle and other manmade perils (see pp.29-33).

broken open first. They seemed unable to open these eggs themselves, and showed no interest in even attempting to do so. It could be that hedgehogs have been blamed for clearing up nests where the eggs have been broken open by other predators. Hedgehogs are also partial to various fruits, especially grapes and apples, though this is not a significant part of their diet.

Hedgehogs have very poor eyesight and rely heavily on their acute hearing and sense of smell in order to locate and catch their prey. Earthworms are located by sound: a hedgehog will stop and put its head down and then pull a worm out of the ground. This behaviour is instinctive since even hand-reared animals will soon learn to catch worms this way. The glutinous slime on a slug's body makes a hedgehog's mouth and paws sticky, so hedgehogs have learned how to remove the slime by rolling the slug along the ground backwards.

Hedgehogs are nocturnal animals and, unless ill, are rarely seen out in the daylight. The majority of the night is spent actively foraging, interspersed with short naps. During the day, the animals sleep in their

A hedgehog's sense of smell is far more important than its eyesight.

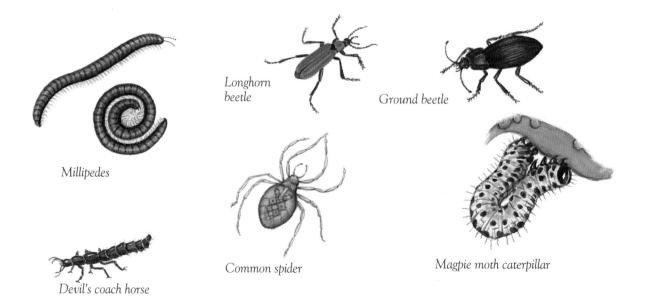

Millipedes

Longhorn beetle

Ground beetle

Common spider

Magpie moth caterpillar

Devil's coach horse

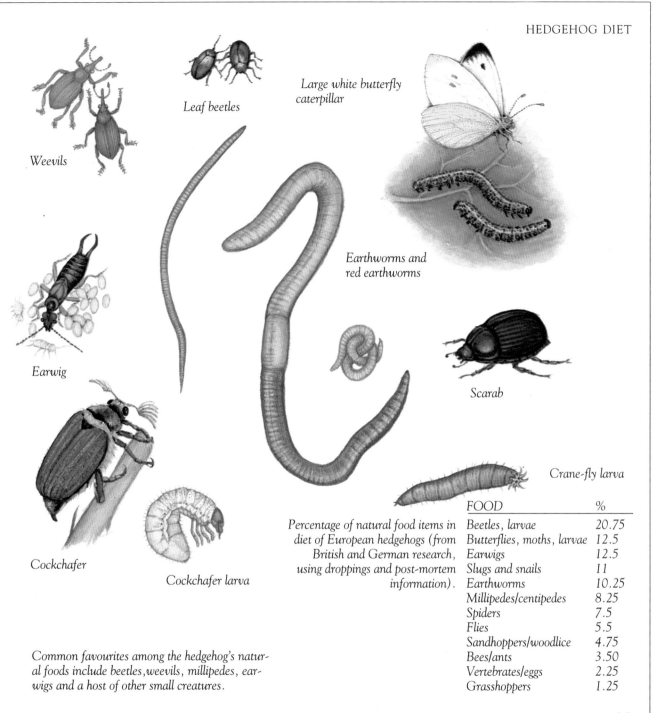

Weevils

Leaf beetles

Large white butterfly
caterpillar

Earwig

Cockchafer

Cockchafer larva

Earthworms and
red earthworms

Scarab

Crane-fly larva

Percentage of natural food items in
diet of European hedgehogs (from
British and German research,
using droppings and post-mortem
information).

FOOD	%
Beetles, larvae	20.75
Butterflies, moths, larvae	12.5
Earwigs	12.5
Slugs and snails	11
Earthworms	10.25
Millipedes/centipedes	8.25
Spiders	7.5
Flies	5.5
Sandhoppers/woodlice	4.75
Bees/ants	3.50
Vertebrates/eggs	2.25
Grasshoppers	1.25

Common favourites among the hedgehog's natural foods include beetles, weevils, millipedes, earwigs and a host of other small creatures.

23

nests. A nest is composed of dried leaves or plucked grass which the animal collects in its mouth. The hedgehog then grooms the leaves into place with its spines and paws until a compact dome is formed. Alternatively, they may use the burrows vacated by other animals such as rabbits. In summer or in warm climates, hedgehogs may not make such well-constructed nests; instead, they find sufficient cover in clumps of long grass. Nests may be located wherever there is sufficient shelter from the elements. Common sites are under brambles or brushwood, in log piles or in burrows among sand dunes. In the winter, when the hedgehog goes into hibernation, the construction of a well-situated and robust nest may mean the difference between life or death.

Hibernation

Contrary to popular belief, a hedgehog's hibernation is rather more than just a lengthy sleep. It is a complex process of energy conservation in which the animal's metabolic rate, cardiovascular system, and respiratory rate all slow right down to the minimum level required to preserve life. A hedgehog deep in hibernation can easily be mistaken for dead since it will be very cold and still, and may not breathe for long periods. It will be curled up and will bristle when touched, whereas a dead one will be uncurled and unresponsive to touch. During this time, the hedgehog lives off its fat reserves, so it must have reached a critical weight (at least 600 grams) before entering hibernation in order to have a good chance of surviving the winter.

A hedgehog's typical nest, or hibernaculum, for winter hibernation.

Hibernation periods vary according to climatic conditions. In warmer climates, such as New Zealand, hedgehogs often do not need to hibernate at all or at least only briefly. In Europe, hibernation usually commences in October and lasts until March or April, depending on the weather. During this time, hedgehogs have periods of activity and may even change nests, but such activity is very costly in terms of energy expenditure and so is kept to a minimum. As spring arrives, they slowly arouse from their hibernation, and the males get ready to search for a mate.

Reproduction and Rearing

In the northern hemisphere, the breeding season for the European hedgehog is from May to September, though this can vary slightly according to the weather. The gestation period is generally between 30 and 40 days. Female hedgehogs may have two litters within a breeding season: in May or June and in August or September. Litter sizes vary from one to eight. (Jane has found that four is the average litter size in Dyfed in rural Wales, with some variation between town and country areas. They tend to be bigger in and around towns than in the country – see p.20.)

If very distressed or threatened around the time of giving birth, female hedgehogs may desert or kill their young and may even eat them. Consequently, there is a very poor success rate for captive breeding of hedgehogs. However, the WHH has a very good record – numerous litters have been born and successfully reared there. The females make very good mothers; but because they recognize their offspring by scent, they may desert the nest if their young are touched by humans. The mother rears her young alone, without any assistance from the male. The young stay with the mother until they are weaned at around 41 days of age, and throughout this period they will receive antibodies from the mother's milk.

Between six and eight weeks of age, the youngsters leave the nest and are completely independent of their mother, who takes no further interest in them. By now, they will have learned to find food, and must gain sufficient weight before winter to enable them to hibernate successfully; they need to weigh at least 600 grams. This is more of a problem for those born late in the season, except in warmer climates, where the hibernation period is shorter. Some youngsters are "orphaned" when their mother goes into hibernation before they are ready to be weaned. Without human intervention these autumn orphans will have no chance of survival.

Surviving youngsters lead solitary lives with little interaction with others of their kind, even their siblings. Fighting is rare, as it seems hedgehogs generally prefer to avoid each other altogether, perhaps to prevent competition over food. Hedgehogs will fight in captivity. Jane has witnessed females fighting each other in the wild, and has also seen them fighting off amorous males. The general pattern of avoidance continues until the youngsters reach sexual maturity between eight and twelve months of age.

The rather noisy affair of hedgehog courtship can easily be misinterpreted as a fight, with much aggression from the female towards the male. The whole courtship may last hours, with the female snorting loudly and frequently rebuffing the male's advances, until she finally relents and allows him to mate with her. It has often been suggested that the female flattens her spines during copulation, but eyewitness accounts report that the female's spines remain bristled. Nevertheless,

These three orphans were rescued at one and a half weeks of age, when their nest in a compost heap was attacked by dogs. The coloured tags are used to identify each individual.

Hedgehog defence

The hedgehog's spiny coat makes a formidable defence against a variety of potential threats. The spines are actually modified hairs and are extremely resilient. When the hedgehog is relaxed, all the spines point backwards, so you can easily run your hand over the animal without being speared. At the first sign of impending danger, the hedgehog will erect its spines and may then run away or freeze, relying on its spines for protection. Then it draws the spines down to cover its face, feet and tail, thus defending the most exposed and vulnerable parts. Hedgehog reflexes are extremely quick, so this all happens in the blink of an eye. If danger still threatens, the hedgehog will then curl up completely, making itself into an almost impenetrable ball of spines. The spines are now bristled and point in many different directions, creating a very prickly problem for any potential predator.

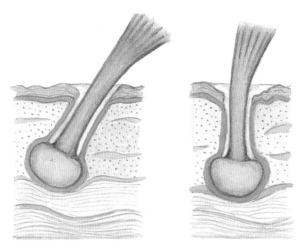

Enlarged view of spine roots in skin.

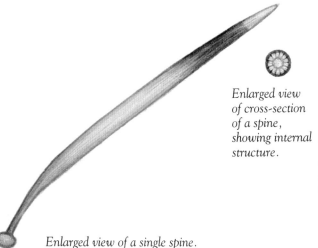

Enlarged view of a single spine.

Enlarged view of cross-section of a spine, showing internal structure.

When a hedgehog is relaxed, its spines lie flat (above left) and point backwards (below left). When the hedgehog is threatened, the spines become erect (above right) and point in different directions (below right).

27

Jane has seen females that were submissive and flattened their spines, although on other occasions they remained bristled. When erect, the male's penis is extremely long for an animal of this size: it extends from the middle of the abdomen to beyond the nose. It may be that the length of the male's penis allows him sufficient distance from the female's spines to make intercourse bearable! Once mating has taken place, the couple go their separate ways, the male taking no further part in the reproductive process.

Natural Hazards

With their armoury of spines to protect them, hedgehogs are invulnerable to a wide variety of potential hazards. The hedgehogs you see today have changed little since the species came into existence many millions of years ago. The species survived the changes in climate and habitat because of its remarkable capacity to adapt. With such a good survival record, there has been no need for it to evolve further as a species. Why change a design that works? It has few natural enemies because many predators have become extinct or are few in number.

In Britain, the badger is the hedgehog's greatest natural predator. Its efficiency in sniffing out hibernating hedgehogs – badgers take more hedgehogs in winter – is aided by its canny ability to uncurl them. The badger puts its claws into the small gap in the tightly curled spiny ball and pulls it open to get at the vulnerable underside. After its meal, all that will remain of the hedgehog is skin and spines. Both foxes and jackals are swift enough to kill hedgehogs before they have time to roll up. In general, foxes tend to take sick or small hedgehogs, as well as eating dead ones, as do polecats, mink, grey mongooses, and birds of prey such as owls and buzzards. Nestlings may be lost to smaller carnivores.

The highest mortality rate is during the winter hibernation. Badgers account for some of these losses; the rest are likely to die because they do not have sufficient fat reserves to see them through the winter. In order to reach the spring, a hedgehog must not only have gained sufficient body weight (at least 600 grams) prior to hibernation, but must also have constructed itself a robust nest in a safe location. Youngsters are particularly vulnerable at this time. Most hedgehog deaths occur before the animal has reached its first year.

In addition to the problem of surviving cold winters, a hedgehog is vulnerable to excessive heat, although it will encounter such conditions only in warm climates and in captivity. It can only sweat from the underside of its body, so in very hot weather it needs to find somewhere cool to lie. When overheated, a hedgehog will spread itself out as flat as it can to allow as much heat loss as possible.

Hedgehogs have no fear of falling, perhaps because of the shock-absorbing effect of their spines. However, this lack of fear, combined with an inquisitive nature, does lead many to their deaths. If there is anything, natural or otherwise, for a hedgehog to fall into then you can be sure it will fall into it sooner or later!

The road sign outside the WHH, where 80% of admissions between 1986 and 1994 were due to manmade hazards. Around 18% were due to natural causes and 2% to unknown causes. In areas of greater human density, casualties from manmade hazards will clearly be higher.

Not So Natural Hazards

Apart from mishaps, predators and natural disasters (e.g. fire and flooding), hedgehogs have not had a great deal to worry about. Until the arrival of *Homo sapiens* on the planet (and hedgehogs were here long before us). Manmade hazards and perils fall into four main categories: environmental, chemical, mechanical, and deliberate killing or damage. It is hard to estimate the effect of these on the hedgehog population, either to date or in future. However, one thing is sure: the impact of such an array of new problems for the hedgehog coming within a relatively short period of time is considerable.

Environmental effects include destruction of habitat and shortages of food. As human populations have increased, more and more land that was once a haven for wildlife has been turned into roads, agricultural land, housing sites, and shopping centres. Unlike many species, and again due to their capacity to adapt and survive, hedgehogs have found a way to live in an urban environment. However, there is evidence to suggest that this is not without cost to their general health, since country hedgehogs in Dyfed are generally healthier than their town-dwelling cousins (see pp.19-21).

Hedgerows, where they are still in place around fields cultivated by agricultural machinery, can be dangerous places for nesting hedgehogs – the hedges may be carved up by farm machinery. Hedgehogs are now

29

Hazards to hedgehogs

The inquisitive nature of hedgehogs, combined with an apparent lack of fear when it comes to falling, means they are particularly accident-prone. The range of hazards confronting them is extremely varied, as the illustrations on these pages show.

Mr Wiggly was poisoned by formaldehyde after falling into a dog loo and was treated successfully with homeopathy and healing.

Drains can become traps if the cover is removed.

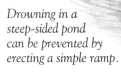

Drowning in a steep-sided pond can be prevented by erecting a simple ramp.

Discarded or stored lobster pots are perfect traps for hedgehogs, too.

Garden strimmers kill or seriously maim many hedgehogs every year.

Slug pellets containing metaldehyde or methocarb (and the slugs which have eaten them) are poisonous to hedgehogs.

Hedgehogs easily become entangled in any kind of discarded netting.

A garden fork stuck thoughtlessly into a compost heap or haystack can kill or maim a nesting hedgehog.

Always check bonfires for nesting hedgehogs before you light them.

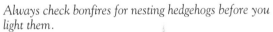

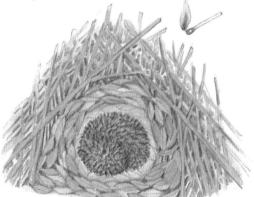

Hedgehogs that fall through the bars of a cattle grid can climb to safety if you have already placed a ramp in the chamber below.

31

rare in arable areas; it is only in less heavily cultivated areas, such as the area of Wales which is home to the WHH, that hedgehogs can still live relatively safely in the countryside. Death by starvation when food is short can be classed as a natural hazard for all species. But as more and more habitats are destroyed, food shortages will increase, particularly for hedgehogs whose main prey species are eradicated by farmers.

The ever-increasing range of pesticides and other chemicals applied to the land and to crops pose a major threat: because hedgehogs eat many of the creatures targeted by pesticides (e.g. slugs, beetles, and caterpillars), they too can fall seriously ill and die. Since many of the chemicals are not easily eliminated from the system, but are stored in the liver and in the fat, the effect of ingesting them will be accumulative. This could particularly cause problems in winter when the hedgehog lives off its fat stores which contain the residue of deadly chemicals. Adding to the toxic burden on the hedgehog's system are the chemical effects of air and water pollution.

As mentioned on page 29, hedgehogs excel themselves when it comes to falling into things. The list of manmade constructions into which they can tumble is endless: cattle grids, swimming pools, garden ponds, slurry pits, and water troughs, to name but a few. They also seem to have little sense of their body size and are very prone to getting stuck in pipes, drains, cups, and cans. Unable to escape, they will die of starvation if not rescued. They may also injure themselves in their attempts to extricate themselves.

At the WHH, the first casualty of the year is usually a hedgehog caught up in discarded garden netting (e.g. pea netting, tennis nets, and fishing tackle). During the autumn and winter, the net collects leaves into a pile. When the hedgehog wakes in the spring, it sees the pile of leaves; believing it to be a good place to nest, it enters and becomes entangled. The netting can cut into the animal's flesh as it tries to free itself, causing severe injury. It will eventually die of starvation if left.

The worst hazards of all are machines, particularly motor vehicles and strimmers. It is important to be aware that a hedgehog's instinct is to rely on its trusty spines for protection. So hedgehogs are unlikely to try to move out of the way of oncoming vehicles, with disastrous results. In an attempt to deter drivers who deliberately try to hit hedgehogs, the

Even seemingly harmless objects such as breeze blocks can become deathtraps (see Puddles, p.93).

Store engine oil or tar safely in closed containers to prevent hedgehogs from covering themselves.

authorities in Sweden have made it an offence to run over a hedgehog. The strimmer is now competing for the top slot in terms of numbers of hedgehog casualties caused. The injuries are usually severe: often, whole limbs or noses are sliced off. What makes strimmer casualties seem so much worse is that they are avoidable: by always checking long grass for hedgehogs before starting, or even better, by not using strimmers at all.

The deliberate killing, maiming, and trade in wild hedgehogs represents the last category of manmade hazards. Gamekeepers and others who consider hedgehogs to be a menace continue to cull them. In many countries at different times, hedgehogs have had a price on their heads and have consequently been exterminated in large numbers. Many hedgehogs are mercilessly kicked and battered to death in the name of sport or fun. Recently, a nest of hedgehogs was disturbed by a group of young school children who trod and jumped on the nestlings, killing them all. Sadly, such stories are far too common. It is hard to punish the perpetrators of this abuse since the loopholes of the law allow them to get away with it more often than not, on the grounds that the hedgehog was technically "free to walk away".

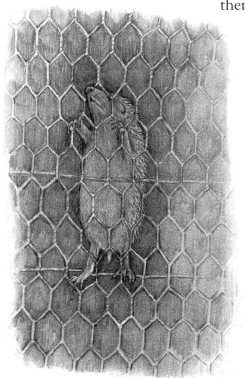

Equally unjustifiable is the increasing trade in wild hedghogs as pets. Whilst some hedgehogs are bred in captivity to be sold as pets, more often they are taken from the wild. In Egypt, for example, it is common for hedgehogs to be taken from the wild and sold in the markets of Cairo. And recently, hedgehogs have been imported into the United States – ostensibly for scientific purposes – and sold as pets.

Butch shows how hedgehogs like to climb chicken mesh fence; they seem blissfully unaware of the dangers. Butch's behaviour shows that he has recovered his health and is ready to be released back into the wild.

CHAPTER TWO

Caring for Hedgehogs

It is not always easy to tell if a hedgehog is sick. People with good intentions often disturb a perfectly healthy animal, or else unwittingly take a mother away from her babies, because they think the hedgehog is ill. This chapter gives guidelines on how you can assess a hedgehog's condition and how you can provide care if it is ill.

Since hedgehogs are nocturnal creatures, you will rarely see one out and about in daytime, unless it has a problem. They do not come out to "play", neither do they "sunbathe". People who contact the WHH saying they have been watching a baby hedgehog sunbathing in their garden are probably witnessing a very sick hedgehog that is suffering from hypothermia and spreading itself out in the sun in a desperate attempt to get warm. This phenomenon can be seen anywhere, particularly in rockeries where the warmed rock helps to heat the animal.

As a general guide, if you see a hedgehog out in the daylight, there is probably something wrong. It requires help, particularly if it is a youngster lying out in the sun (although such cases are often too sick to survive by the time they are rescued). An adult female could be a nursing mother taking a break from a particularly demanding litter of babies who have all finally gone to sleep, thus allowing her a moment to sneak out and crunch a few snails. Two such mothers living in the hedgehog garden at the WHH would come out in the early morning and eat all the snails they could find before returning to their broods. They also ate the shells, perhaps for a nutrient, such as calcium. So, put out extra food for nursing mothers and add a vitamin and mineral supplement containing calcium.

If you are in doubt as to whether such an adult female (see p.47) needs help, it wouldn't hurt to keep her for 24 hours to make sure she is

Whitie was admitted to the WHH as a three-and-a-half-week-old orphan and lived for many years in the hedgehog garden. He was treated by homeopathic vet, Christopher Day.

34

all right. Then put her back where you found her if she turns out to be healthy. If she is sick or injured and needs hospitalization for more than 24 hours, then you must find her babies and bring them in as well. (Use gloves when you pick up the babies so that they retain the scent that their mother recognizes.) She will not have moved far away from the nest: search thoroughly and listen out for telltale squeaks.

Blind hedgehogs also stray out in daytime because they cannot tell the difference between night and day. They are unlikely to survive in the wild because they cannot see dangers such as traffic and often hibernate in the wrong season. Also, they are unlikely to meet others of their kind because they are out and about when most hedgehogs are asleep. They will be happiest in a hedgehog-friendly garden (see pp.61-3) with a sighted hedgehog – who is also nonreturnable (see pp.64-5) – whose presence will stimulate normal behaviour.

Uncurling a Hedgehog

If you decide to take a hedgehog into care, you must examine it thoroughly to discover what it needs. This is no problem if the hedgehog cooperates with gentle handling, but if it is curled up, you will have to uncurl it. The fact that it is curled up is encouraging, because it means the animal is strong enough to do so. A hedgehog that is in a state of collapse or very dehydrated cannot curl up. Usually, hedgehogs are reluctant to uncurl only if they have been abused or if they have wounds on their undersides.

The following method of uncurling a hedgehog is the one Jane finds most effective and least stressful to both hedgehog and handler! It is important to take your time with this procedure (see also p.39) in order for it to be effective. Approach the hedgehog calmly and confidently, and make sure all your movements are slow and gentle. Have some food ready to offer the hedgehog

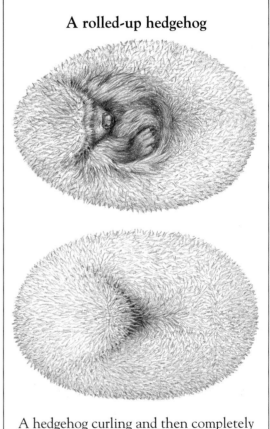

A rolled-up hedgehog

A hedgehog curling and then completely curled into a tight ball reveals the V shape which shows where its head is.

when it has uncurled. Hold the prickly ball up and look underneath for a V shape. This is where the head is; the point of the V is above the snout and the base of the V is above the back of the head.

Having worked out which end is which, hold the hedgehog the right way up over a table with the head downwards. Now very gently rock it to and fro. Eventually, the hedgehog should start to stick its nose out – let it smell the food you have ready. Keep rocking it and talk softly to it. The two front feet should start to appear. When the front legs are well extended, slowly move the animal towards the table and allow it to put its front feet down. Carefully move your hands away and the hedgehog should start to put its back legs down as well.

Once the animal is fully uncurled and on the table, try getting it to take an interest in the food. This will give you an opportunity to move your hands underneath to pick it up and examine it. Hold it up and look underneath it – don't turn it upside down or handle it roughly, otherwise it will curl up and be very reluctant to uncurl again. And never hold a hedgehog by its legs because you could injure it.

On occasion, Jane will use an anaesthetic gas under veterinary supervision to help her uncurl a reluctant hedgehog. Usually, she finds that, with gentleness, patience and a dose of homeopathic Arnica or Aconite, hedgehogs cooperate and allow dressings or even splints to be changed without becoming stressed.

How Old is the Hedgehog?

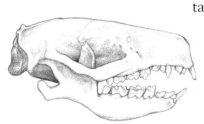

The hedgehog skull shows the blunt teeth designed for eating insects. Like the rings in the trunk of a tree, a hedgehog's jaw has growth lines. The number of lines indicates its age.

A back paw (left) and a front paw (right) show strong claws and pads. The more worn these are, the older the animal is.

To determine an infant's age, look at the illustrations on pages 54-5, which show the stages of development from birth to four weeks. Once a hedgehog has reached maturity, age determination is more difficult – the most accurate way requires the animal to be dead, since it involves making a section through the jaw bone. Because a hedgehog's metabolism slows down during hibernation, the bone shows a line each time hibernation (i.e. one winter) occurs. Like tree rings, these lines can be counted. This method would be less reliable in countries

37

with milder climates, such as New Zealand, where hedgehogs frequently do not need to hibernate in the winter.

A hedgehog in its early years shows few clues as to its age. An adult in its first year will have slightly smaller claws, complete with their original points, which have not yet been worn down. The pads of the feet will also show little wear. A second-year hedgehog will be slightly bigger and is likely to be in good condition. From three years and upwards, age determination is much more difficult. The condition of the teeth can give a rough guide – an animal with long white teeth will be younger than one whose teeth are worn down. However, a hedgehog living in an area where the soil is gritty will quickly wear down its teeth when feeding and consequently may appear older than it is. Older hedgehogs may have a build-up of tartar on their teeth, as is the case with elderly dogs and cats. A hedgehog with a skin problem, due to disease or parasitic infestation, may seem older because of its poor appearance.

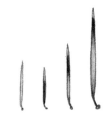

Hedgehog spines from left to right: first white spines; second-stage first brown spines; third-stage spines; adult spines. All actual size. (See also pp.54-5.)

Assessing a Hedgehog's Health

You can assume that a hedgehog taken out of the wild and handled by humans will suffer from shock. To remedy this, give the animal homeopathic Arnica at once, unless something else is more urgently indicated by its condition. The Arnica will be needed anyway if the animal has been injured and will help it to cope with the stress of being handled.

The urine test stick (the Bayer Diagnostics Multistix 10SG – see Resources) is an invaluable aid when you need to assess the health of a hedgehog. Normal analysis readings for a range of factors to be found in urine are given below.

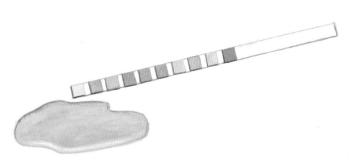

Normal Urine Readings

*Leucocytes – negative.
Nitrite – negative
Urobilinogen – normal 3
Protein – 0.30
pH – 6.0
Blood – negative
Specific Gravity – 1.030
Ketones – negative
Bilirubin – negative
Glucose – negative*

Jane and Lamie demonstrate how to uncurl a hedgehog (see also pp.36-7). Lamie had to have an emergency operation to remove a badly infected, severed back leg after she was hit by a strimmer.

First hold her with her nose pointing down towards a table. Gently rock her to and fro.

When she starts to stick her nose out, continue to rock her gently.

When she reaches out towards the table, let her touch it.

Gently place the hedgehog down on the table.

39

When a hedgehog is awake, it is normally active and constantly sniffing; its respiration rate should be between 50 and 110 respirations per minute (r.p.m.). The normal respiration rate for a sleeping hedgehog is 25 to 50 r.p.m. During hibernation, this rate drops to 13 r.p.m. or less; there will even be periods when the hedgehog ceases to breathe for an hour or two. Normal heart rate is 120-170 beats per minute (b.p.m.) when active or during sleep, with an average of 140 b.p.m. Again, this drops during hibernation to as low as 5 to 10 b.p.m. (The above figures are based on research on many hedgehogs at the WHH.)

Unless the hedgehog is unconscious (see p.41), observe and check the animal's general appearance and posture. Make some notes as you carry out the examination; they will help later, both in selecting appropriate remedies and in monitoring the hedgehog's progress.

The following is a checklist of questions to ask if you find an ailing hedgehog:-

- Are its eyes bright?

- Is it alert and interested in its surroundings?

- How well and how fast is it breathing?

- Is it cold?

- Is there any blood, either on it or coming from it? If so, check where from.

- Is it restless or reluctant to move?

- Can you see any external wounds?

- Can it walk properly?

- Are all its limbs intact?

- What does it smell like? (Hedgehogs normally smell earthy.)

- What is the condition of its spines and fur? Are there any bald areas?

- Are there any skin lesions?

- Can you see any parasites (see pp.73-7)?

- Is it dehydrated?

- Has it passed any stools or urine? If so, what do they look like (see pp.46-8)?

- Is anything (e.g. netting, plastic) wrapped around a part of its body?

Fluid Loss

If the hedgehog seems to be in an advanced state of dehydration, then give it some fluid as a matter of urgency. The easiest way to check for dehydration is to test the skin's elasticity. When you pinch an area of your skin and then let it go, the skin should go straight back to normal rather than remaining pinched for a while. Pull up a section of the hedgehog's spines and then let it go and see if the skin springs back into place. If it doesn't, the animal is dehydrated. Try it on your own skin as a comparison. If in doubt, give fluid to the animal anyway since it won't do any harm. Use Lectade or Dioralyte (see p.98). If neither of these is available, give water with a little honey or glucose mixed in. Warm the liquid to body temperature before giving it, especially to a baby hedgehog or one that is very cold or collapsed. If they are not too sick, hedgehogs will normally drink water on their own.

Collapsed Hedgehogs

If the hedgehog is in a state of collapse or even unconscious, you will need to get some fluid into it very soon or it will die. An animal in this condition is likely to be very cold, so warming it up is also a priority. A dose of Aconite will usually help to reverse hypothermia very quickly: it is rather like turning on the animal's central heating! Carbo veg and Arnica are also useful (see Appendices for selecting the best remedy and Chapter Three on homeopathy). Putting the hedgehog on a purple plate (see p.90) will be beneficial whilst you work out a remedy.

Often, the remedy will arouse the hedgehog enough so that it can suck at a syringe. If it is still unable or unwilling to do this, tube feed it with some fluid (see p.52). If tube feeding is new to you then enlist the help of an expert (e.g. your vet). A hedgehog that needs tube feeding is in a very critical condition and will need constant monitoring – give it some fluid every hour until it is back to normal.

Going to the Vet

Always take a sick hedgehog to the vet for a diagnosis. Enquire locally for a vet who has a particular interest in treating wildlife. (Find out whether the vet will charge you for treating hedgehogs.) The vet may

41

know nothing about hedgehogs, so pass on the 'phone number of a hedgehog expert the vet can contact for further information if necessary. Before going to the vet, clean any wounds, remove maggots, give the hedgehog some fluid if at all possible, and keep it warm. If the hedgehog is very sick, taking it to the vet is more of a priority.

Be sure you understand the diagnosis and treatment your vet offers you. Check its suitability for hedgehogs with an expert before undertaking the treatment. Tell the vet if you would prefer to use homeopathy under the vet's supervision. Alternatively, find a homeopathic vet via the BAHVS (see Contacts, p.106). With collapsed animals, vets often inject saline and steroids. The WHH has found that tube feeding warmed Lectade is more effective than injecting saline and that very sick hedgehogs given steroids are less likely to survive than those treated homeopathically. Steroids also interfere with the action of homeopathic remedies and have a suppressive effect on the immune system, so try to avoid any steroids if possible. If the vet does give a steroid to your hedgehog, request that an antibiotic be given at the same time.

Snuffles shows the various telltale signs of hedgehogs which are sick: flat appearance of spines, staring of fur, and dull eyes. The closeness of his back legs and his curved back show how desperately thin he is.

Snuffles was admitted to the WHH as a juvenile, suffering from severe lung worm infestation complicated by pneumonia. Homeopathic treatment, combined with a safe wormer, saved him.

Care of Wounds and Injuries

If you find a wound on your hedgehog, take a note of how it smells. Hedgehogs normally have an earthy smell. An offensive smell probably means the wound is infected, particularly if there are maggots in it. Septic sores may look like wounds but could just be caused by the animal scratching a heavy burden of mite or ringworm. These parasites also cause bald patches or missing spines and it is common for both to be present (see Chapter Three).

Clean any wounds with warm salt water; use one teaspoon of salt to 500ml of water. Check all wounds for maggots; if present, remove them by flushing with a syringe full of salt water. Some people recommend using a hairdryer on maggot-infested wounds, but this is very stressful to the hedgehog. If the animal is dehydrated, the use of a

When Snuffles recovered, he showed the signs of a well hedgehog: bristled, healthy spines; shiny and big bright eyes; thick, smooth fur; and nicely rounded body revealing an ideal weight.

Hedgehogs are often covered in fly eggs or maggots on arrival at the WHH. This three-week-old orphan was so cold that flies mistook her for dead and laid their eggs on her. These must be removed at once.

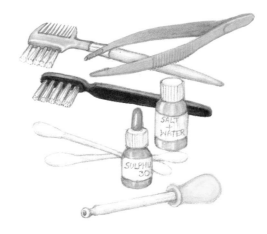

Close-up of blow fly, fly eggs, and maggot.

To remove fly eggs and maggots safely, you will need the following: small combs and brushes; tweezers; cotton buds and dropper. Clean the wounds with salt water and give the hedgehog a dose of homeopathic Sulphur 30c. A dentist's water jet is particularly useful for flushing out maggots (see Resources).

43

hairdryer will make things worse. A dentist's water jet is an excellent tool for flushing out maggots.

A conscious hedgehog with a maggot on its body is likely to be irritable, restless, and snorting. The animal will not relax until all the maggots have been removed. Use a magnifying glass in conjunction with an artificial daylight bulb to spot maggots. Maggots may also be found in or around the hedgehog's anus or genitals, so check these areas, too. Also look for maggots and fly eggs inside the ears, around the eyes, and in the armpits and mouth.

Don't put ointments on wounds containing maggots. And don't use anti-maggot powders because they are very toxic, even in very small doses. A word of warning about hedgehogs and ointments: if the ointment appeals to the hedgehog's palate it will bite at the area and may do serious damage. This was demonstrated by Wilbur, a young hedgehog at the WHH who bit off two of his toes after ointment for ringworm was put on his foot. Even though he screamed from the pain, he didn't realise that his biting was causing it. He was given Arnica and then put on Hypericum each day, and the ointment treatment was stopped. As long as he had his dose of Hypericum he ceased biting himself. Had this remedy failed to work, Wilbur would have had to wear an Elizabethan collar (see p.46) until his foot had healed. (For information on remedies, lotions or ointments for external wounds, see Appendices.)

If you find a hedgehog caught up in discarded netting, plastic from carry packs of beer, or a can, carefully remove the object. It may have cut into the flesh, in which case be careful not to do any further damage. The best instrument for removing fine nylon embedded in the flesh is a pair of desuturing scissors (your vet will have these since they are designed for removing stitches). A hook in the lower blade helps you get under the nylon so you can cut it.

If you suspect a bone fracture, seek the advice of a vet, who may wish to X-ray the hedgehog. The vet will advise you on splinting the

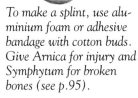

To make a splint, use aluminium foam or adhesive bandage with cotton buds. Give Arnica for injury and Symphytum for broken bones (see p.95).

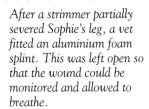

After a strimmer partially severed Sophie's leg, a vet fitted an aluminium foam splint. This was left open so that the wound could be monitored and allowed to breathe.

injured limb. In some cases, the vet will need to anaesthetize the animal to apply the splint. You can make splints from household items, such as two cotton buds or lollipop sticks held on with sticky tape or plaster tape. Specially made aluminium strips with foam lining are ideal. Be careful not to make the splint too tight, otherwise it will restrict circulation; nor too heavy because it could then pull on the break.

For compound fractures, where the bone has broken through the skin, thoroughly clean the area before applying a dressing or splint. Leave a gap so you can monitor any cuts. Hedgehogs with fractured limbs often make the original injury worse by walking around on the damaged limb and by the resultant wounds becoming dirty and infected. Hedgehogs rarely rip their splints off, but if they do you will need to fit the hedgehog with a cardboard Elizabethan collar (see p.46).

Burns are a common problem, especially from bonfires or firework displays. Always check bonfires for sleeping hedgehogs before lighting them (see also p.31). As with other wounds, burns should be cleaned thoroughly before applying an appropriate ointment or lotion (see p.94). And give remedies (e.g. Causticum) internally to help the burns heal faster. Treat the hedgehog for shock, too, and be sure to give it plenty of fluid. Serious burns should always be looked at by a vet.

Zorba's broken forearm needed a lightweight splint made from cotton buds. It was firmly fixed and taped at her elbow to stop it slipping (see Hattie, p.92).

An L-shaped splint made from aluminium foam is fitted to Woolie's broken ankle after she was hit by a car.

Care of Juveniles

A juvenile hedgehog is one that has left the nest and is not yet fully mature (i.e. between six to eight weeks and twelve months old). Juveniles deserve a special mention concerning their care because they are the most vulnerable to stress and therefore the most difficult to treat and rehabilitate successfully (see p.62). This is perhaps because they are more aware of their environment and circumstances than infants and not as strong or experienced as adults. They are rather like sensitive teenagers! Because of this, be extra careful when

45

handling them and minimise stress as far as possible. Frequent repetition of remedies for shock and stress will help considerably (see Appendices). If they are hyperactive (i.e. very restless), you may be deceived into thinking they are fine when they are actually very ill. Such hyperactivity is often followed by collapse and death, so it requires urgent treatment (see p.96).

Bowels and Bladder

Make sure the hedgehog is emptying both its bowels and its bladder every day. Keep a note of the colour and consistency of feces and urine, and observe any changes (see urine test stick, p. 38). This will help with diagnosis and prescribing the correct remedies. If possible, send samples of stools and urine for analysis, either to the vet or a vet investigation laboratory. If the hedgehog has not passed anything for 24 hours or more, it may well have a problem and you will need to administer the appropriate remedy fairly quickly (see Appendices). A hedgehog with a full bladder which is unable to pass urine will be very uncomfortable, a situation usually rectified rapidly by a dose of Apis.

Baby hedgehogs up to the age of three to four weeks require external stimulation in order to empty their bowels and bladder. Their mothers normally do this in the wild by licking around the tail. In the absence of the mother, it will be up to you, so after each feed, gently clean around the hedgehog's bottom and massage the entire area with a cotton bud soaked in baby oil (see p.48). If the baby has been abandoned for some time before its rescue its bowels or bladder may be blocked or very full. This should be attended to promptly because the hedgehog will not drink until it has passed something.

The colour of a baby's stools will tell you something about its health (see p.47). Bright emerald-green stools are due to a recent lack of food. After the hedgehog has been on a goat's milk diet, they should change to a pale greenish blue. Adding meat as well will make the stools firmer and brown. If the stools become dark and runny, or if they contain blood, the hedgehog will require some treatment since it may have coccidia or enteritis. Similarly, if the stools contain large quantities of

Elizabethan collars will stop hedgehogs from biting their wounds or their dressings. Make the collar with shiny card of about 280-300gsm (mail-order catalogue covers are ideal) and waterproof tape. Follow the dimensions below. When fitting, make sure the animal's ears are well forward and the collar doesn't cut into its neck.

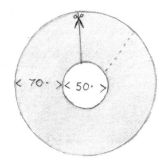

What sex is it?

Try to establish the hedgehog's sex at once, because if it is female she may be pregnant or nursing young, which will need to be found. Give the hedgehog some food and whilst it is eating, gently slip your hand underneath its middle. Feel around the fur in the centre of its belly. If it is a male, you will find his penis. If there's nothing but fur, it is a female. Both sexes have two rows of nipples. Sex differentiation is more difficult with baby hedgehogs because the penis is further back, nearer the anus, at birth. It will move forward as the hedgehog grows. Sometimes, the remnants of the umbilical cord may be mistaken for the penis sheath.

Hedgie – a female

HEDGEHOG DROPPINGS

From the top down:
- *Normal healthy dropping of a hedgehog fed on dog food and dried insect mixture.*
- *Droppings with ends that are dark green, stringy and gel-like can indicate worms.*
- *Dropping of a hedgehog that is not digesting its food properly, either because of illness, antibiotics, unsuitable food, or worms/flukes.*
- *Green water may be caused by stress-related infections such as E.coli.*
- *Healthy droppings of an orphan fed on correct/suitable milk substitute.*
- *Loose droppings may indicate lack of roughage in diet. If dark and smelly, there may be enteritis or infection.*

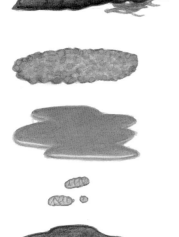

Frostie – a male

47

undigested food, treatment will be required, possibly with a change of diet. Dark emerald or olive-green stools could be caused by cow's milk in the diet or could also be an indication of an infestation by lung worm or intestinal worms. Pink, fleshy-coloured stools are generally caused by worm infestation or infection. Mucus in the stools can mean the gut lining is ruptured. (For adult stools, see p.47.)

Hygiene

Scrupulously clean all feeding utensils and any surfaces which have been in contact with hedgehogs. A proprietary disinfectant suitable for babies will suffice for this unless you have a patient with a contagious infection, in which case use a veterinary disinfectant that kills viruses. Keep separate utensils for each animal, or clean them thoroughly between patients.

If you suspect an infection, isolate the hedgehog from other animals. Wash your hands thoroughly before and after handling a hedgehog. Burning incense sticks helps reduce the spread of airborne infections by killing bacteria in the air. It also seems to relax the hedgehogs! Ionisers, too, help purify the air and are especially useful if you live in a town. They can bring benefit to hedgehogs with breathing difficulties.

Feeding Hedgehogs

Feeding adult hedgehogs in captivity is relatively easy because they thrive on readily available sources of food (e.g. dog food) with a little supplementation. Clearly, the best diet for any hedgehog is what it would normally eat in the wild: beetles, worms, slugs, snails, and various insects (see pp.21-4). If you have only one or two hedgehogs in your care you could probably manage to collect sufficient quantities of natural foods for their needs.

However, since hedgehogs can pick up parasites from molluscs, insects and worms, it is probably better to buy insects such as meal worms, meal worm beetles, waxworms, buffalo worms and crickets from live food suppliers (see p.51 and Resources). Red fisherman's worms and compost worms are also a good food source and easily available from pet shops and garden centres respectively. These captive-bred insects are best because they are parasite-free.

A baby orphan is unable to empty its bladder and bowels, so you must toilet it yourself before each feed. With a cotton bud dipped in baby oil, gently tickle the hedgehog's genital region (see also p.46).

48

Easier alternatives are available for those too squeamish to feed live food to a hedgehog. Always keep in mind what hedgehogs would normally have access to in the wild. Organic meat is ideal – it contains no artificial additives or unwanted residues (e.g. from pesticides or drugs). If this is unavailable, or too expensive, good quality non-organic meat is still preferable to tinned dog or cat food, which is the next best option.

Of the tinned foods available, first choice is Dene's Healthmeal: its ingredients are the most natural and it contains no chemical additives (if your pet shop doesn't stock it, try your local health food shop). Any tinned dog or cat food will do, but the top-of-the-range ones (Pedigree Chum or Kit-e-Kat, for example) are better quality, as generally speaking you get what you pay for. Choose varieties without fish and concentrate on white meat varieties (i.e. chicken, turkey, rabbit) because these are closer to a hedgehog's natural food sources.

Cook raw meat before feeding it to your hedgehog to avoid passing on parasites. And mince it up – hedgehogs have neither the dental equipment nor the digestive system to cope with large chunks of meat! Liver is not recommended because it contains toxins and is too rich. Mix the cooked minced meat with dried insect food ("soft bill" insectivorous bird food – see Resources) or with cereal such as wheat flakes. This will provide the hedgehog with the roughage it needs.

It is important to remember that overfeeding your hedgehog can be fatal. An adult hedgehog weighing between 700 and 900 grams needs about 100 grams of tinned food daily. Divide this into at least two meals. Hedgehogs tend to overeat if given the chance, so don't be guided purely by your patient's appetite! Hedgehogs weighing over 1400 grams should be given restricted rations and plenty of exercise. An overfed hedgehog will drink a lot and will eventually die of liver or kidney failure.

Dried hedgehog food can be obtained by post from the British Hedgehog Preservation Society. Such food is particularly useful for hedgehogs with breathing troubles that cause an impaired sense of smell: the food contains strong-smelling meal worms. However, if your hedgehog has trouble digesting it, switch to one of the foods above.

Eggs are a natural part of the hedgehog's diet yet should be used, either scrambled or raw, in moderation. Organic free-range eggs are best. Hedgehogs are often partial to quail's eggs, which are also very good for them. They make an ideal treat and can be given raw; you will need to crack them open first. Your hedgehog may like kitchen scraps which you can add to its meals (e.g. chopped up vegetables or fried food, but never pork or bacon). Hedgehogs like fruit, too; bananas are a favourite and are also good for the digestive system. Only give milk in small amounts to adults and avoid giving cow's milk at all; goat's milk is more easily digested by hedgehogs.

Hedgehogs are as individual with regard to their dietary preferences as they are with everything else. Experiment to see what your hedgehog likes and dislikes. A hedgehog's natural diet is highly nutritious, so in captivity it is important to supplement the hedgehog's diet with extra vitamins and minerals (see p.98) to make up for any lack in the diet. Parsley and watercress, seaweed supplements and slippery elm are all beneficial. Esbilac, a tinned milk substitute, is fortified with extra vitamins and minerals and is especially good for both young and convalescing hedgehogs. (For supplements and substitutes, see Resources.)

Always make fresh water available to your hedgehog. Put it in a low non-spill dish, which he will soon get dirty. Hedgehogs seem inca-

Quail's and hen's eggs can be given to hedgehogs as part of their natural diet when in captivity. You will need to break them open.

Common snails and slugs are often eaten by hedgehogs. These carry parasites such as fluke and lung worm, so it is best not to feed them to captive hedgehogs (see p.48).

50

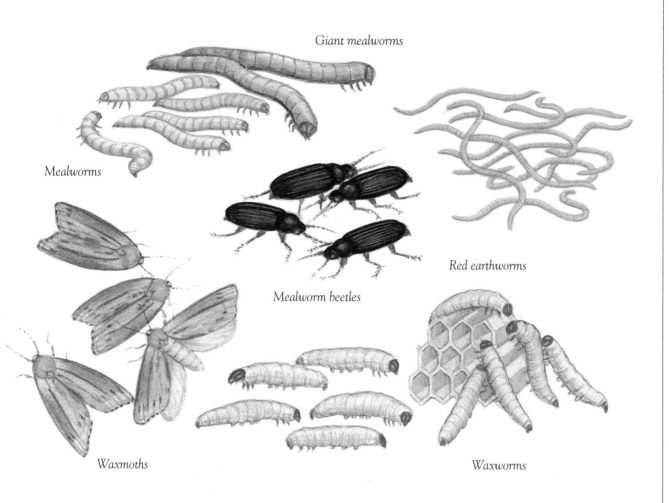

Giant mealworms

Mealworms

Red earthworms

Mealworm beetles

Waxmoths

Waxworms

Hedgehogs in care can be given a rich variety of worms and insects as part of a natural diet. All the creatures above are available from live food suppliers (see Resources).

51

pable of using water bottles designed for rabbits or guinea pigs and prefer to drink natural water (e.g. from ponds) rather than tap water. So make sure you filter tap water first, or else give bottled water. Placing a quartz crystal in the water helps to purify it (see p.84).

Feeding Orphans

Caring for a baby hedgehog is not to be undertaken lightly. First make sure your orphan is warm enough and attend to any urgent medical problems. Before giving the youngster some food determine how old it is (see pp.37-8 and pp.54-5). Remember to keep all feeding utensils for the hedgehog sterile, as you would for a human infant. Proprietary baby bottle sterilising solutions seem to be safe enough, but sterilising by steaming or boiling is the most natural method.

    Very small hedgehogs need to be fed with a pipette or a syringe. As a temporary measure, you could use a paintbrush or a spoon. All food and drink should be warmed to body temperature. A baby bottle warmer allows you to warm liquids to precisely the right temperature. The hedgehog must not become dehydrated, so give a suitable liquid regularly: at first, an electrolyte replacement such as Lectade or Dioralyte is best (see p.41). If these are unavailable, give a small amount of warm water with a pinch of glucose in it. Start the youngster on this fluid replacement before giving any milk. If the milk causes the hedgehog to develop digestive troubles, put it back on a fluids-only diet for 24 hours.

    The best substitute for hedgehog's milk is Esbilac, a tinned liquid milk replacement containing vitamins, minerals, and egg yolk in a skimmed milk base (see p.104). Second choice as substitute is sheep's milk. If neither of these products is available, try goat's milk and mix in some goat's or sheep's colostrum (one part colostrum to two parts goat's milk). If the hedgehog's stools are not firm, increase the proportion of colostrum. The colostrum contains antibodies which will help your orphan, which has not received its full quota over the 41-day suckling period, to acquire immunity to various diseases. Finally, add a vitamin and mineral supplement to the milk each day.

Murphy was 2 weeks old when he was found unconscious on the roadside. He was so cold that flies had mistaken him for dead and laid eggs inside him. After Aconite 200c and a spell in an incubator, he could soon suck Lectade from a syringe (see above and p.53). Maggots in a head wound, in his ears and even in his penis were flushed out with salt water. He had one more dose of Aconite and then 2 doses of Sulphur 30c to help rid his body of toxins.

Cow's milk is not recommended for rearing hedgehogs. Its constituents are in different proportions to those in hedgehog milk, rendering it very hard for all hedgehogs to digest. Digestive upsets are common on a cow's milk diet and powdered milk can cause blockages. At the WHH, Snorty, who was two and a half weeks old, died after taking powdered baby milk; post-mortem results showed that he had not digested the milk properly. In an emergency, when nothing else is available, make up a mixture of skimmed milk and egg yolk with added vitamins and minerals until a more suitable alternative can be found.

Once you have prepared a suitable mixture and warmed it to body temperature, very gently feed the hedgehog. Give one drop at a time; be very careful not to get the mixture up the hedgehog's nose and into its lungs. Do not be too generous with each feed; little and often is best. Overfeeding could cause stomach or chest problems. Given the chance, hedgehogs like to eat more than is good for them at one go. Remember to help baby hedgehogs to empty their bowels and bladder between feeds and on their arrival (see p.46 and p.48), otherwise they won't drink. Weigh the baby daily to make sure it is gaining weight. If it is not, treat as an emergency. The following is a guide to the feeding requirements of hedgehogs of different ages:

Birth to three days old: Feed 1 to 2 ml of milk substitute (see p.52) every 2 hours, including through the night.

Three days to one week old: Continue as above, gradually increasing the interval between feeds to 3 hours. If the baby is doing well you can safely leave it through the night, but don't leave more than 6 hours between feeds.

One week to two weeks old: Feed 2 to 3 ml of milk at 3-hour intervals.

Two to three weeks old: Feed 3 to 5 ml of milk at 3 to 4-hour intervals.

Three to four weeks old: Feed 5 to 6 ml of milk at 3 to 4-hour intervals. Introduce a small dish of milk so the baby can learn to lap on its own; as it learns to do this, reduce the hand feeding.

STAGES OF DEVELOPMENT

These illustrations show the development and growth of baby hedgehogs from birth to four weeks of age. Jane has been fortunate enough to witness the births of three litters of hedgehogs at WHH and she has meticulously recorded the baby hogs' progress. The various changes in colour which the babies undergo are as shown.

At birth: *Nipper, shown here, is blind, deaf, and bald. The skin on his back has a layer of fluid beneath the surface, covering the prickles like a large water blister. He could crawl as soon as he was born. Length 50-100mm. Weight 7-25g.*

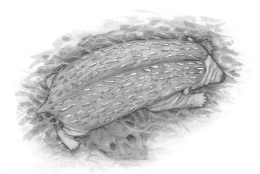

One hour old: *Nipper has an even coat of white prickles pushing through his skin (the fluid has dispersed). Babies attract their mother's attention by emitting a shrill call, which is surprisingly loud for their size.*

36 hours old: *On Podgy and his two siblings the second coat of prickles can be seen emerging. These are dark brown with white tips and are much smaller and narrower than adult spines. The nestlings are unable to curl up, but if disturbed will jump up and jab their spines into any intruding object.*

One week old: *Squeaker is still blind and deaf, his white prickles still longer and more noticeable than the brown ones. A few small whiskers emerge on the end of his snout. At 11 days, he will be able to curl up.*

Two weeks old: *Murphy has more second- than first-coat prickles, causing him to look darker. He has a sparse covering of short fine hairs, like stubble, mainly on his snout. His eyes could start to open any day now; then his ears will begin to open. His third coat of prickles – larger, stronger, and more like adult prickles – will begin to emerge around this time.*

Four weeks old: *Fluffy has lost the rounded, puppy-like appearance of her snout, which has now become pointed like an adult's. She has a good coat of spines and thick brownish fur, making her skin invisible. Her milk teeth have erupted so she can take solid food. She is alert and active with a bristly coat and generally looks much like a miniature adult. She should weigh approximately 85 to 130g.*

Three weeks old: *Patch has a good set of third-stage prickles, with few white prickles left. Her eyes and ears are open and her first upper incisor teeth begin to erupt. She has a good dense covering of short brown fur.*

55

Four to five weeks old: Continue to give hand feeds, but less often, and give a dish of milk. Leave out a small, non-spill dish of water. Offer some solid food now; a small dish of puppy or kitten food liquidized with water, a whole warm and freshly scrambled egg, or some liquidized boiled chicken are all suitable starters.

Five to six weeks old: Give a fresh dish of milk daily, if the baby still wants it. Phase out hand feeds. Provide a small dish of water and a dish of liquidized food – add a vitamin and mineral supplement and mix in some cereal or dried insect food twice daily. (If this does not interest your orphan, try putting some milk on top of the food.) Adding enzyme supplement (e.g. Acidophilus or Lactobacillus – see Resources) will aid digestion, as will live goat's milk yoghurt.

Six to eight weeks old: Gradually phase out milk feeds because this is the end of the weaning period. Give a small dish of tinned puppy or kitten food mixture twice daily. Each feed should consist of a large tablespoon of puppy food finely mashed and mixed with a little breakfast cereal or dried insect food and a vitamin and mineral supplement. Give him a dish of fresh water each day.

Eight weeks old: At this age young hedgehogs normally leave their mother's nest permanently. They will weigh about 350 grams. Their mother will have taught them how to forage for beetles and other insects. Those that are hand-reared will need some help learning to find food for themselves. Take your youngster into the garden on warm dampish evenings to encourage it to forage. It should pounce on slugs and snails or sniff out worms and beetles. If it fails to get the idea at first, try giving it a few meal worms (from pet shops). Remember, hedgehogs are nocturnal, so only encourage them to come out in the evening. Avoid using a white torch light as this may cause an association between motor vehicle headlights and food; use a red light instead.

You can provide larger meals now and gradually introduce adult dog food. Start by mixing some dog or cat food in with puppy or kitten food, and each day increase the dog food and decrease puppy food. The meat should be mixed with some "soft bill" insectivorous bird food. If this is unavailable, mix some cereal in with the meat. The juvenile no longer needs milk. Give the vitamin and mineral supplement (see p.50) once a week. As an occasional treat, try some cooked chicken or turkey. Seedless grapes and bananas are also favourites (only give a small piece of banana or one or two grapes at a time). Provide fresh water daily. Once your hedgehog is schooled in foraging, and weighs at least 600 grams, you can release it (see pp.62-4).

Homes for Hedgehogs

If you are nursing a sick or injured hedgehog back to health, it is vital to make its environment as comfortable and hygienic as possible. This aids the animal's recovery because it keeps any stress to a minimum. The following advice and guidelines regarding indoor and outdoor housing, and a hedgehog-friendly garden, are those that have worked best at the WHH. You can improvise with whatever materials you have available, keeping in mind the hedgehog's natural lifestyle and requirements. If you take in hedgehogs on a regular basis, try to acquire a thermostatically controlled incubator (see Resources).

A cardboard box makes a fine indoor home for your hedgehog, but it becomes sodden very quickly, so you will need to change it every day. Bear in mind that hedgehogs can climb out of boxes with short sides. Avoid using a banana box for babies because they may get their heads stuck in the oval holes in the sides! The best arrangement is to use two boxes – one for sleeping and an outer one for feeding and as a toilet area. Cut a small hole in the side of the "bedroom" box to allow the hedgehog access and put a lid on the bedroom to create a dark resting place. This arrangement is easy to keep clean and is inexpensive. If you are keeping several hedgehogs or are looking after one for a long time, you may want something more robust, such as a stackable plastic crate or a plastic carrying case designed for cats.

The ideal bedding for a sick hedgehog is a towel or a jumper. These are easy to wash and keep clean. A woolly jumper or teddy bear fur is best for babies. If your hedgehog has an injury, use a towel for its bedding but not hay or sawdust – hay gets wrapped around the feet (and causes problems to all hedgehogs), and both hay and sawdust can interfere with wounds and injuries. You can use sheets of newspaper if you change them daily at the very least; but avoid shredded paper because hedgehogs can get tangled up in it. Hamster bedding may be adequate if made from natural fibres, but the amount an adult hedgehog needs may be too expensive. Hamster bedding is not suitable for babies because they tend to lie on top of it, away from their heat source. Warm bedding is particularly vital for a baby hedgehog. Using a jumper as an envelope so the baby can nestle inside is the best way to keep its body heat in. Alternatively, give the baby a teddy bear to snuggle under.

Very sick or baby hedgehogs will need some additional heat in their nests. A direct heat source works better than an overhead lamp. A hot water bottle is ideal, but make sure it is well covered and not too hot or too heavy. Alternatively, use a plug-in heat pad designed for pets. A hot water bottle may act as a mother substitute for babies and, incidentally, seems to confuse some adult males into thinking they are in the company of a female and so they try to mate with it!

Sick or injured hedgehogs need to be kept in a warm quiet room with soft lighting and a supply of fresh air. It is very important to keep their environment clean, changing any soiled bedding as soon as possible. Babies need to be kept in a germ-free environment at a temperature

A new resident moves in to the hedgehog house at the WHH (below). The plans to make such a house are shown opposite. All measurements are in millimetres. The sides are made of 20mm-width pine; all other parts are 12mm plyboard. Legs should be screwed together in pairs. You will also need brass screws, two brass hinges, a latch, and a padlock.

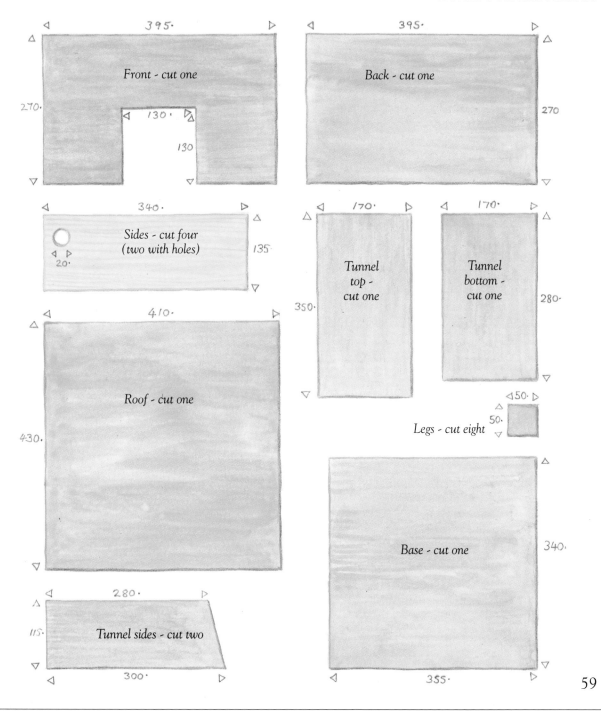

◁ 395· ▷

Front - cut one

270·

◁ 130· ▷

130

◁ 395· ▷

Back - cut one

270

◁ 340· ▷

Sides - cut four
(two with holes)

135

20·

◁ 170· ▷

Tunnel
top -
cut one

350·

◁ 170· ▷

Tunnel
bottom -
cut one

280·

◁ 410· ▷

Roof - cut one

430·

◁50· ▷

Legs - cut eight

50·

Base - cut one

340·

355·

◁ 280· ▷

Tunnel sides - cut two

115·

◁ 300· ▷

59

of 35°C (95°F), which is a hedgehog's normal body temperature. Air ionisers are very helpful; Jane has found that, since she has been using them at WHH, inmates do not develop respiratory problems. And coloured light bulbs can help with a variety of problems (see pp.87-8).

Outdoor Housing

Once your hedgehog is restored to health, and before it is ready to be released, you should house it outside in a rabbit hutch, providing the weather is warm enough. Even the smallest rabbit hutches on the market are big enough for one hedgehog. Alternatively, make your own hedgehog house (see pp.58-9). Whichever you choose, place the house on grass if possible so the hedgehog can dig in the soil. Ark runs designed for rabbits are ideal. Remember, hedgehogs can climb so make sure the run either has a top or that the sides are curved over at the top.

If you wish to create a nesting place for wild hedgehogs, either for hibernation or for a mother with young, then build the house from wood so that it is predator-proof and highly durable. Put a few dry leaves inside the box for nesting. The house should be big enough to keep one hibernating hedgehog or a mother with a litter. Place it in a quiet shady spot in your garden where the hedgehogs won't be disturbed. Make sure the entrance faces away from prevailing winds (see pp.58-9).

Once your hedgehog house is ready, place some food (e.g. a dish of dog food or meal worms) in the entrance. Hopefully, you will soon have a hedgehog in residence. Obviously, if you live in an urban environment where your garden is enclosed, you will have to introduce one. Only introduce nonreturnables (see pp.64-5) and make sure your garden is safe (see p.61). Never introduce hedgehogs to areas where they do not already live and never take healthy hedgehogs from the wild.

Do not disturb your new resident or open the box because the occupant is likely to leave and not return. A mother with young may desert or even kill her babies if disturbed. And when your hedgehog emerges from hibernation in the spring, you can clean the house. The best time for this is the beginning of April in the northern hemisphere before a mother hedgehog is likely to want the house for rearing her babies. Use a mild disinfectant and, if necessary, give it a good sprinkling with a hedgehog-friendly flea killer (see p.77).

Creating a Hedgehog-friendly Garden

To attract and keep hedgehogs in your garden you need to ensure that your garden has the right habitat and is safe. Leave some areas of your garden undisturbed and create other areas which provide the hedgehogs with cover. Piles of leaves, compost heaps, brambles, and wood piles are all ideal places for hedgehogs to nest. A wide variety of plants will attract a similarly wide variety of insects to appeal to the palates of your local hedgehogs!

A garden pond not only provides hedgehogs with a supply of water for drinking and swimming but also a profusion of insects to feed on. You could also put out food yourself. Don't worry about supplementing the hedgehogs' diet with dog or cat food (but not cow's milk). It will not stop them from foraging for their natural food. In fact, during the build-up to hibernation, it can help them gain sufficient weight to enable them to survive the winter.

Safety is a major priority in your hedgehog-friendly garden. Do not use chemical insecticides, pesticides, etc. on your garden; organic methods for controlling pests and weeds are much safer, not only for hedgehogs but for all living things. In particular, avoid slug pellets; instead, use organic methods of slug control, such as beer traps (see Resources for leaflet).

Make sure hedgehogs can climb out of your pond easily. Naturally sloping sides present no problem, but if the sides are slippery you should put some chicken wire down to give the hedgehogs something to grip on. If the sides are vertical, erect a ramp in the pond. Avoid putting plastic netting over ponds during winter to keep leaves out: hedgehogs can easily get tangled and drown. In general, be careful with netting. Store fruit netting out of a hedgehog's reach and furl tennis nets well above ground when not in use.

It is important that you dispose of litter carefully, especially anything that hedgehogs could get caught or stuck in (e.g. cans, pots, plastic from carry packs of drink). Make sure all holes, drains, and pits are securely covered. Before lighting bonfires check them for nesting hedgehogs. And check long grass for hedgehogs before you start cutting it with a strimmer (see also pp.30-1).

Back to the Wild

Releasing a hedgehog you have nursed back to health is immensely satisfying. Monitoring by the WHH has shown that hedgehogs released back into the wild often thrive. Females have been identified with offspring, making their original rescue and subsequent rehabilitation even more worthwhile. And adult males add to the local hedgehog population. To give your hedgehog the best possible chance of surviving, make sure it is fully fit and able to forage well for itself before you release it.

Juveniles are too vulnerable to be released. Since most hedgehogs die either in the nest or before their first birthday, it is better to wait until juveniles are fully grown before releasing them because their chances of survival will become much higher. Hedgehogs released in the autumn need to weigh at least 600 grams in order to withstand hibernation. Any hedgehog below this weight should be kept through the winter and prevented from hibernating.

A hedgehog-friendly garden contains the following (reading clockwise from top left hand corner):
- *Herbs to attract bees and hoverflies*
- *Hedgehog feeding station by French windows*
- *Local stone crazy paving, with insects in cracks*
- *Bird table encourages birds and wildlife*
- *Cottage garden flowers attract bees, hoverflies and butterflies*
- *Barbecue rather than open fires*
- *Ideal nesting site under shed*
- *Half grapefruit skins collect slugs and snails around strawberries*

The pond at the WHH which has been made safe for hedgehogs. The depth in the middle is 45cm. Note the shallow, gently sloping sides.

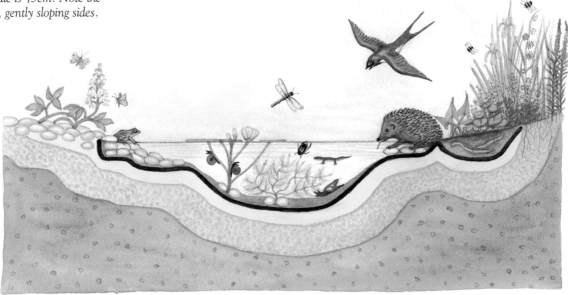

62

- Organic compost bins make nesting sites
- Beer trap collects slugs and snails around lettuce
- Pea and strawberry netting fixed above hedgehog height
- Incinerator burns garden waste
- Brambles and nettles attract caterpillars and make nest site
- Natural pond with shallow sides
- Bog and marsh, plus other wild habitats
- Woodland flower area
- Corn field annuals attract insects
- Meadow flowers and grasses are food plants for caterpillars and many insects
- Oak woodland and hedgehog houses
- Old logs attract insects and fungi
- Mixed hedge of native trees and bushes
- Lawn for hogs to catch worms on
- Shrubbery, including Buddleia attracts bees and butterflies
- Drystone walling is home to insects and lizards
- Hedgehog ramps fitted to pond
- Separate pond for fish since they consume much of the natural flora and fauna

A young, hand-reared hedgehog needs to learn how to forage for itself and should be encouraged to make a nest. Keep it outside for a while in a hedgehog house or rabbit hutch with a run to help it acclimatise to life in the wild. Feed it as before but provide a tray full of soil, leaves, insects, worms, slugs, and snails. It will soon get the idea of scratching around in the soil to find the food. Instead of a blanket, provide leaves and paper tissues with a few short strands of hay to allow it to practise nest-building. After a couple of weeks, it should be more than ready for life in the wild.

A casualty that comes into care as an adult also needs such rehabilitation. Make sure it is eating some insects and is bright and bristly, of sufficient weight, and with normal droppings (see p.47). Then look for a suitable location for its release.

The first priority is to find a place where other hedgehogs are living. Choose a site well away from badger territories and as far away from main roads as possible. Your hedgehog will settle best in an environment similar to the one from which it came: release a town hedgehog in a town and a country hedgehog in the country (see pp.19-21). Ideally, choose an area with trees, hedgerows, and meadows and where farmers continue to use traditional methods. Try to keep to the area where the hedgehog was found: if it has an infection of which you were unaware, then you will avoid the risk of introducing the infection to a new area.

Release your hedgehog during warm weather when there are plenty of insects around. Put food and water out each day for a couple of weeks: your hedgehog is likely to lose weight at first, so any extra food increases its chances of survival. Protect the food dish from cats with a piece of cork or well-sanded plywood and a pebble on top.

Nonreturnables

The primary aim of all wildlife rescue and rehabilitation is to release animals back into the wild once they are healthy. In some cases, when the animal would have no chance of surviving, this is not possible. Unlike many other species, hedgehogs can still live comparatively normal lives if kept in a suitable environment that you have created.

Each hedgehog needs to be assessed individually. What are its needs and survival prospects? Females unable to cope with giving birth

Bringing a hedgehog out of hibernation

On occasion, you may have to bring in a hibernating hedgehog for care. During hibernation, the animal's metabolism slows down so much that it may be mistaken for dead. A good way to check is to poke it gently. If it is alive, its spines will bristle strongly and it will snort or hiss and take a deeper breath, all because you have activated its response to predators. Hedgehogs only hibernate curled in a ball, so if you find one spreadeagled or lying on its side it is not hibernating (see p.34). It is important to bring a hedgehog out of hibernation very slowly to allow its body to adjust. Put the hedgehog somewhere warm and leave it to come round in its own time, just checking its progress from time to time. Leave out some food and water so it can help itself when sufficiently awake.

and rearing young are nonreturnables. So, too, are individuals that cannot curl up because they will not be able to hibernate or protect themselves adequately. Other nonreturnables include those that are deaf or completely blind (one-eyed hedgehogs can survive in the wild) and those that have lost their all-important sense of smell. Albino or white hedgehogs should be kept in a safe, walled garden (to keep them from taxidermists!).

Hedgehogs which have lost a front leg cannot dig or climb on their own, but those without a back leg can thrive – first check that they can climb out of ditches and dig sufficiently well before releasing them. Remember, hedgehogs with missing limbs tend to get sore stumps or other problems.

The best place for keeping long-term casualties is in a walled or well-enclosed garden that is safe (see pp.61-3). How they cope with the presence of humans depends on how tame they are. Try to keep more than one hedgehog in such a garden, especially if one is blind (see p.36).

If you notice your hedgehog continually running around in circles, look for mites or an infection (see Circling, p.94). If the animal appears to be healthy, this circling behaviour could be caused by stress or boredom brought on by lack of space. Also, newly blind hedgehogs often circle like this for a while.

Put out some food and water for your hedgehog every day. When winter approaches, be sure to provide plenty of nesting material and suitable sites for nests, or else make a hedgehog house (see pp.57-60). If your hedgehog is not big enough, or for some reason is unable to hibernate (e.g. it cannot curl up), keep it indoors through the winter. Keep it warm, well fed, and don't allow it to hibernate. When the spring returns, let it go back outside. Whilst it is far more satisfying to release them back into the wild, hedgehogs kept in a safe walled garden can thrive for many years and this is surely preferable to no life at all.

CHAPTER THREE

Hedgehog Homeopathy

One of the difficulties in treating wildlife with conventional veterinary drugs is that they have side-effects, which are not always known. What is safe for one species is not necessarily safe for another. And since such drugs will have been tested on a species physiologically different from any wild species, it makes the prescribing of drugs to wildlife a process of trial and error. By contrast, homeopathy and the other alternative therapies mentioned in this book are not tested on animals and can be given to any species of wildlife safely, with no side-effects. Also, the ill effects of veterinary drugs can be considerably reduced by the concurrent use of appropriate homeopathic remedies.

Homeopathy is a natural system of healing which works by stimulating the body's capacity to heal itself. Treatment is in the form of remedies, available as liquid or tablets. Remedies are selected according to the main principle of homeopathy, i.e. that like cures like. Any substance able to produce a particular set of symptoms when given in sufficient doses can also be used to cure a similar set of symptoms. Each remedy is tested, or "proved", to discover the range of symptoms it will produce when given in sufficiently large doses. These same symptoms are recorded and the resulting remedy picture can be used as a guide to the curative use of the remedy.

In order to avoid side-effects, the remedies are given in the minutest possible doses. This is achieved by subjecting the remedies to a process of potentisation, involving repeated dilution with vigorous shaking, or succussion, between each dilution. Although scientists have not yet ascertained exactly how this process works, it seems that the process of potentisation releases the healing properties of the substance. The more a substance is subjected to dilution and succussion, the more

Humphrey was very ill on arrival at the WHH. He was starving, had one eye damaged, and both eyes were congested and weeping. Cuts on his abdomen were full of maggots. Euphrasia helped his eyes to heal and Sulphur 30c helped him recover from the toxic effects of the anti-maggot powder he was given.

66

potent it becomes. Thus the higher potencies are the most powerful, even though at these potencies they contain no detectable trace of the original substance. Remedies made in this way produce no side-effects and are non-toxic, even if the original substance itself is poisonous in material doses. This allows such deadly poisons as Belladonna and Arsenic to be used beneficially in homeopathic potency without danger.

The WHH has been using homeopathy successfully since 1990, after Jane had found that many hedgehogs were vulnerable to the side-effects of conventional veterinary treatments such as antibiotics. This particularly applied to very young or very sick animals. Jane also had problems with antibiotic resistance. Furthermore, a number of hedgehogs' lives were saved by homeopathy when the animal would not have been expected to survive under conventional treatment or which suffered from a condition for which no drugs were available.

Homeopathic remedies are also beneficial when a clear diagnosis is unavailable. This is because remedies are prescribed according to the "picture" of symptoms which an animal presents, i.e. the patient is treated not the disease. Homeopathy can be used prophylactically against certain diseases or to build up resistance to parasites. It can aid the body in ridding itself of unwanted toxins (e.g. from pollution, poisons, or drugs). Overall, hedgehogs cared for homeopathically not only have a better chance of survival, but when released into the wild (see p.62) will be far healthier and so less likely to develop further problems.

Any condition to which hedgehogs are likely to succumb can be treated homeopathically. Always work closely with a vet, a homeopathic vet if possible (see Contacts, p.106). In difficult cases, if your knowledge of homeopathy is insufficient to meet the hedgehog's needs, you may need to resort to antibiotics or other drugs. Your vet will advise you when this is necessary. Such a course is preferable if it means saving a hedgehog's life. Homeopathy can still be invaluable in aiding the hedgehog to regain health as quickly as possible and to help it overcome any side-effects from the drugs given.

A few hedgehog casualties are too badly injured to survive or else arrive too late to be saved. However, homeopathic remedies can considerably lessen their suffering during their last moments. Since using homeopathy at the WHH, no hedgehog has died in a distressed state or

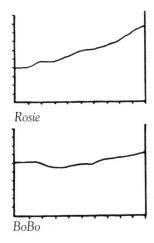

Rosie

BoBo

The graphs show how homeopathy compares with allopathic treatment of baby hogs (the hardest to treat because of their sensitivity to drugs, which can prove fatal). The growth curve of Rosie, a 3-week-old who was treated homeopathically, rises much more steadily than BoBo's, who was treated without homeopathy. The graphs, which are typical of many cases, show that Rosie did not lose weight in the vital first few days and gained weight more rapidly than BoBo.

obviously in pain; most of the terminal cases die peacefully in their sleep. Many hedgehogs, apparently on their death beds, have revived after homeopathic treatment – so homeopathy is always worth trying, no matter how ill your hedgehog appears to be.

How to Use Homeopathy

Homeopathic remedies are inexpensive and easily available. The best results come from remedies obtained at a homeopathic pharmacy (see Resources). Liquid remedies are the easiest to administer to hedgehogs, although tablets work just as well. If you buy liquid remedies, order the potency you require in a dropper bottle with a pipette, not a pourer restrictor. Remedies work fastest when put on a hedgehog's tongue. One drop of liquid is sufficient. If you give more than this, don't worry – it's the potency that counts, not the quantity, and anyway it only counts as one dose if administered all at once. If you can't put the remedy on the tongue, try just inside the animal's lip, or put a drop on its nose.

Tablets can be given, too. Some hedgehogs eat them, others need them crushed up. If administering a whole tablet, hold it with tweezers against the animal's front teeth or in contact with its nose for a minute. Alternatively, crush the tablet between two spoons and put some of the resulting powder in its mouth, or dissolve the powder in a little bottled water and then administer it with a dropper. If the hedgehog is curled up, put a dose of the remedy on a clean piece of skin between the spines on its back. Although you can give the remedy in a teaspoon of food or drink so that it is all taken at once, it is preferable to give it on its own.

The remedy starts to act as soon as it is in contact with the hedgehog. Even if the animal spits out a tablet, it will most likely still produce a reaction, so don't give another dose. If you are unsure, then wait a while; if a response from the remedy fails to show, repeat the dose.

Remedies are sensitive to handling. Try not to touch them; use tweezers and, if you drop a tablet, throw it away and use another. Store remedies in a cool, dark place away from sunlight. Their action will also be halted, or antidoted, by a number of strong-smelling substances, such as camphor, menthol, eucalyptus, peppermint, and coffee. So, be particularly careful to keep both remedies and hedgehogs undergoing treatment away from anything containing these substances.

69

Selecting a Remedy

In order for homeopathy to work effectively you must select the right remedy for your hedgehog. You need to give the remedy which most closely matches all the symptoms presented by your hedgehog. The key to finding the best remedy is to determine how a particular disease or symptom manifests in a particular hedgehog. Ten different animals suffering from the same condition may each need a different remedy, depending on how the condition affects them.

Build up as comprehensive a picture as possible of how your hedgehog is behaving and the symptoms it is presenting. Refer to the notes you made when assessing your hedgehog (see pp.38-40). This is known as "taking the case". Make a note of anything unusual about the animal's appearance or behaviour. See how it reacts to different stimuli (e.g. warmth, cold, light, dark, noise). What sort of mood does it seem to be in; is it irritable, anxious, placid? Even seemingly irrelevant things you observe may be crucial in pinning down the best remedy.

Once you have a full symptom picture of your hedgehog and its ailments, turn to the Repertory (see Appendices). Note all the remedies included under each symptom. Now turn to the Materia Medica (see Appendices) and go through each remedy to see which ones match the most symptoms. Compare each remedy with the whole picture of your hedgehog. Whichever remedy fits the symptom picture of your hedgehog most closely is the one to select.

This is the most practical way to choose your remedies and you will learn a great deal working this way. In selecting remedies, some people rely more heavily on their intuition while others may even dowse for the correct remedy when no remedy was clear from looking in the Repertory. As long as you cross refer to the Materia Medica to see how well the selected remedy fits the case you can't really go wrong, whichever method you choose.

Potency

The right remedy should work regardless of the potency used. However, you will get a better response if you administer the optimum potency. Since homeopathic remedies are available in any potency, look for the number written after the remedy name. The two commonly available in the shops are 6c and 30c; 6c is a low potency, 30c is a higher potency. Potency is the measure of how many dilutions and succussions the original substance has undergone; the highest potencies are the most diluted – they are very powerful and should be used with care.

If you are new to homeopathic prescribing, it is best to start with 6c and 30c potencies until you are more confident. The 30c is at the lower end of the range of high potencies and hedgehogs generally seem to respond well to it. You will not need to repeat higher potencies as often as lower potencies; often a single dose is sufficient. As a general guide, the more sure you are of the remedy, the higher the potency you can give (there is less margin for error with high potencies). Also, take into account your hedgehog's overall condition; a very weak animal may not be able to cope with a very high potency remedy. In such cases, you would be advised to refer to someone with more expertise in homeopathy, or stick to low potencies and repeat them often.

Dosage and Repetition

Give one drop or one tablet of the selected remedy and potency. Make a note of any changes or responses in your hedgehog, with regard to its symptoms and general demeanour. It is a common response for a patient to feel better in themselves immediately after a remedy, even before any change in symptoms has occurred. If your hedgehog looks brighter and happier or more comfortable, you have made a good choice.

Sometimes, the symptoms temporarily worsen after a remedy. If this occurs when the hedgehog seems to be feeling better, it is a homeopathic aggravation and will soon pass. This is actually a good indication that the remedy is working so don't interfere or you will cancel the effect of the remedy. If your hedgehog's condition has not improved or changed in any way, or has worsened with no sign of it feeling better, you should select another remedy. How long you need to wait in order to see a response depends on the acuteness of the condition. The more acute cases should respond within minutes or at least within an hour. In chronic conditions (e.g. with chronic skin complaints), the response may take days or a week or two to appear .

It is important to give only one dose and not to repeat it until you are sure the effect of the first dose has ceased. The idea is to give the minimum dose needed to stimulate a response and repeat only when necessary. The time to repeat the remedy is when symptoms worsen and the symptom picture remains the same as before. If in doubt as to when to repeat, it is best to wait rather than give another dose too soon. Repeating remedies too soon will actually interfere with the hedgehog's healing process. You may be confused at first, but with practice you will soon get a feel for when a remedy needs repeating.

If the symptoms remain the same when you repeat a remedy (in other words, the remedy does not work or else the effects of it wear off very quickly), you need to give it in a higher potency because the potency you have been using has done as much as it can. Select the next highest potency available and try again. If a repeated remedy still fails to work, or if the symptom picture has changed, you will need to find another remedy that fits the new picture. When treating very acute problems, you may find yourself changing remedies quite frequently to keep up with the changing symptoms.

Once you are satisfied that your hedgehog has responded to a remedy as much as possible, you no longer need to repeat it, unless the animal's condition deteriorates again. In many cases, just one or two doses of a remedy are all that is needed to restore a hedgehog to health. When using a remedy prophylactically (e.g. to give resistance to a particular pathogen) one dose is usually sufficient.

In general, the fewer remedies you prescribe at once the more effective each will be, so try to stick to one remedy at a time until that remedy is no longer helping. However, there are occasions where more than one remedy is needed, such as when a hedgehog has an injury and a parasite problem. In these cases, give the two different remedies as far apart as possible; preferably one in the morning, the other in the evening, but with at least half an hour between them. This also applies if a hedgehog is receiving drugs; here, you may find you need to repeat remedies more frequently as they are used up faster.

If possible, enlist the support of a homeopath or homeopathic vet at the start of a case. Then, if you get stuck, qualified help is at hand. Many homeopaths are willing to advise on prescribing for wildlife (see Resources). And if you are inexperienced, always take the hedgehog to a vet to make sure you do not miss anything important.

Identifying and Treating Parasites

Tackling parasite problems is a priority in hedgehog care. Many hedgehogs admitted to the WHH are already suffering from a heavy infestation of internal or external parasites, or both. Others are made more vulnerable to parasites by their depleted condition when sick or injured. Any parasites present will proliferate rapidly on a weakened animal. The degree to which parasites have taken hold is a good indication of the hedgehog's general condition; the healthier it is, the less likely it is to be heavily burdened with parasites.

Hedgehogs are prone to many different types of parasite. The most notorious is the hedgehog flea (except in New Zealand, where it was not introduced with its host). The stories of hedgehogs and their fleas are exaggerated – many hedgehogs brought to the WHH have no fleas. This flea will not live on any other species, though it may give you a minor bite. Other common external parasites are ringworm, mites, and ticks. Hedgehogs do not suffer from lice.

Many veterinary drugs used to combat parasites are so toxic that they are likely to kill the host as well as the parasite, or at the very least make the hedgehog more ill than it is already. The following information and guidance are the results of alternative methods of combatting parasites which have been tried – and found to work – at the WHH. It is certainly not the last word on the subject because more research needs to be done on non-toxic parasite control. Where infestation is very heavy, it is necessary to give anthelmintics (e.g. fenbendazole) and other drugs, but the concurrent administration of homeopathic remedies enables the hedgehogs to cope with their toxicity better.

There is no set procedure for homeopathic treatment which works for every hedgehog. Remedies which best fit the individual case will do the best work. If you see a remedy picture clearly, then try that remedy first. Homeopathic remedies will not kill parasites in the same way as conventional drugs. They build up a hedgehog's strength so that it can overcome the parasites itself. Parasites will not thrive in a healthy body.

Hedgehogs are not wormed routinely at the WHH because, on examination, droppings rarely contain eggs or parasites. The only exceptions are thin and out of condition hedgehogs, and autumn juveniles. It seems pointless to worm a hedgehog that has no worms, especially since the toxicity of the wormer will destroy the natural intestinal flora. Never give a wormer to a hedgehog under four weeks old. Postmortems at the WHH show that hedgehogs younger than three weeks do not have a parasite burden and have never died from parasites. The youngest hedgehog that died from worms was six weeks old. This suggests that worms are not passed across the placenta.

EXTERNAL PARASITES

If you suspect your hedgehog may be suffering from parasites on the outside of its body, illuminate the animal and, with a magnifying glass, search the skin for anything abnormal. The diagrams accompanying this section will help you identify your hedgehog's problem. If you are suspicious of anything, send a skin and hair sample off to a veterinary laboratory. If you have access to a microscope, you can check spine, skin, and hair samples for mites or ringworm yourself. If one of these parasites is present, it is fairly safe to bet the other will be, too – so treat for both. And pay extra attention to hygiene because some (e.g. ringworm) may be transmissible to humans and other animals.

Ringworm

Flaky skin or patches of missing hair or spines are probably due to mites or ringworm. Sometimes ringworm produces scratching that is so severe it produces sores which may contain maggots. Hedgehogs can be infested with various species of ringworm, some of which fluoresce under an ultraviolet lamp (see Resources). Once you know which ringworm is present you can tell where it is likely to spread to, how bad it is, and how easy it is to treat. The hedgehog ringworm (*Trichophyton erinacei*, see right) does not fluoresce in UV light; and although rare, it is the easiest to treat.

Hedgehogs may heal small infested patches themselves, simply by eating a better diet, supplemented by vitamins and minerals. More widespread infestation needs treatment. Unlike conventional veterinary treatment, which seems unable to prevent ringworm from returning, homeopathy has such an excellent record that the WHH would not use anything else now. The most frequently effective remedies for ring-

M. canis

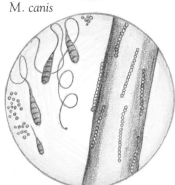

T. mentagrophytes

Four species of ringworm are common in hedgehogs (all drawings are x75 and show macroconidia and a hair with ringworm spores). Microsporum canis (top) causes loss of spines and flaky skin. Trichophytum mentagrophytes (above) leads to loss of spines and hairs, and damage to the claws. Microsporum gypsum (top right) is usually confined to the nose and ears. Trichophytum erinacei (bottom right) causes crusting, loss of spines and hair, and damage to claws.

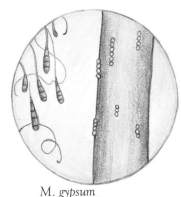

M. gypsum

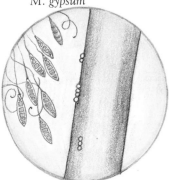

T. erinacei

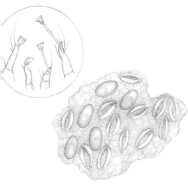

Microscopic mite eggs and shells cluster on hedgehog skin. Adults have suckers or hooks on their feet (left).

worm are Arsenicum, Sulphur, Silica, Thuja, and Bacillinum. If the hedgehog is restless, with flaky skin and loss of hair or prickles, give Arsenicum album 30c. If the hedgehog is hot with dirty, smelly skin and bald patches, give Sulphur 30c. Where abscesses are present and the hedgehog likes to be warm, the remedy most likely to help is Silica 30c. Where there are crusty localized growths, give Thuja 30c.

Give these remedies twice daily until a response is seen (usually within a week). Then stop the remedy and repeat only if the symptoms worsen. Bacillinum 200c once a week helps considerably to build up the animal's resistance to ringworm and other fungal infections.

Dabbing affected areas with garlic juice kills ringworm spores and prevents the parasite from spreading. This should be done twice daily for a week or the ringworm may return. An effective lotion can be made from elder leaves, herb Robert, and garlic. Simmer the mixture for 20 minutes and leave to steep for seven hours before applying. Dress the affected areas with the lotion each day for a week.

Mites

Of the wide variety of mites, some are visible to the naked eye (if you have sharp eyesight); others can be spotted only under a microscope. Look for minute specks of white dust or see if the hedgehog has a generally dusty appearance or flaky skin (flaky skin alone may be ringworm). Mites are often accompanied by a secondary bacterial infection and a mangy smell. *Caparinia tripius* and *Sarcoptes* mites, the latter responsible for mange, are the two kinds commonly affecting hedgehogs. Another is the orange harvest mite, which congregates around their noses.

Larger species can be killed with pyrethrum powder, as for fleas. Garlic will kill mites so garlic or herbal baths are helpful, but they need to be repeated more frequently than chemical baths. Try the elder, herb Robert, and garlic lotion prescribed for ringworm. Give herbal baths daily or every few days until the problem clears. Clean the hedgehog's bedding and house regularly to prevent re-infestation. Give vitamin and mineral supplements and provide a good diet; parasites will not thrive on a healthy body. Sulphur, given at the same time as herbal baths, is the best remedy. Give 30c weekly for three weeks. If heavily infested give a 6c twice daily until the mites start clearing, then give 30c weekly

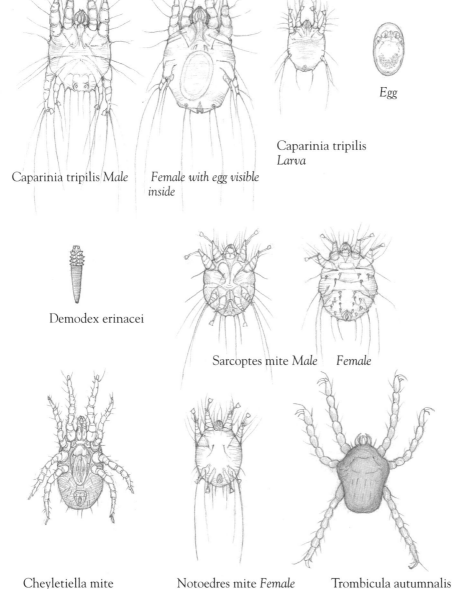

Caparinia tripilis Male

Female with egg visible inside

Caparinia tripilis *Larva*

Egg

Demodex erinacei

Sarcoptes mite *Male*   *Female*

Cheyletiella mite

Notoedres mite *Female*

Trombicula autumnalis

Six hedgehog mite species are shown left (all x50 approx).

Caparinia tripilis *is the commonest, causing loss of spines and hairs, flaky and crusty skin with septic sores. Visible as small, mobile, whitish, dust-like specks.*

Demodex erinacei *live in spine or hair follicles, with symptoms similar to* Caparinia.

Sarcoptes *mites burrow into the skin, causing it to go hard and crusty. Other symptoms are similar to* Caparinia.

Cheyletiella *mites are usually mixed with other mites* Notoedres *mites can cause mange lesions on ear edges and in ears.*

Trombicula autumnalis, *or harvest mite, causes similar (but less severe) symptoms to* Caparinia. *Visible as red mobile dots on the skin.*

Archaeopsylla erinacei

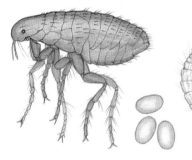

The hedgehog flea with eggs and white larva (all approx x15). Small specks of blood on the base of the spines indicate fleas. The eggs are laid in the hedgehog's nest.

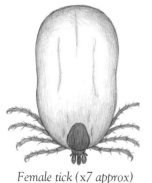

Female tick (x7 approx)

Ixodes ticks are often found around the face and ears. After a blood meal, the white tick turns grey.

until the hedgehog is clear. Other remedies are Thuja and Psorinum. In severe cases, bath the hedgehog in bromocyclen 6% solution.

Fleas

More of a problem in urban rather than rural areas, hedgehog fleas are noticeable because they are so large (see left). You can see them between the spines, where they usually live. If you see fleas jumping off a hedgehog, it means the animal is in a poor state. As a rule, remove or kill all fleas because they can carry disease to other hedgehogs. The following advice applies to all species of flea.

Fleas are relatively easy to keep under control. As a preventative measure, give one dose of Sulphur 30c weekly for three weeks. Give the whole course to keep the animal's resistance up when the fleas' eggs hatch (the eggs incubate for two weeks). The Sulphur appears to make the host less palatable to the fleas. In heavy infestations, give the remedy more frequently until the problem is under control (e.g. Sulphur 6c twice a day for three weeks, together with pyrethrum powder).

Aromatherapy (see pp.90-1) and certain herbs help to deter fleas. They seem to dislike lavender and rosemary, so sprinkle either of these in dried form in the hedgehog's house. Or use a drop of the essential oil.

Because of their big body size and large surface area, hedgehog fleas are more vulnerable to mild insecticides such as pyrethrum (made from the dried flowers of a chrysanthemum). Pyrethrum is sufficiently powerful to kill fleas, and is less toxic than other insecticides. Don't cover the hedgehog in it, just sprinkle a little on the back of the animal's neck so that it doesn't breathe the powder up its nose when it curls up. And don't resort to harsh treatments, particularly products containing dichlorvos and fenitrothion, which are fatal to hedgehogs. If you are unsure about a product, don't use it unless you check first with someone experienced in treating hedgehogs.

Ticks

Ticks are fairly common, particularly *Ixodes hexagonus* (see female, left). Remove ticks carefully – if you leave the head or mouth parts in the skin they could cause infection. Clean the wound with Calendula.

77

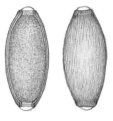

Capillaria erinacei *Eggs*

Capillaria sp. *Eggs* (x450 *approx*)

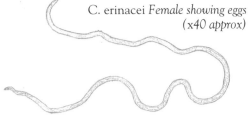

C. erinacei Female (x15 *approx*)

C. erinacei *Female showing eggs*
(x40 *approx*)

Capillaria *Worms*
(*actual size approx*)

Intestinal worms

As many as 1000 of the yellow, lemon-shaped eggs of Capillaria erinacei may be found in a gram of feces. The adults of this thread worm are white and just visible to the naked eye as white whiskers. The intermediate hosts are various species of earthworm.

Another Capillaria lays slightly larger eggs with parallel sides, prominent plugs, and a lacy surface.

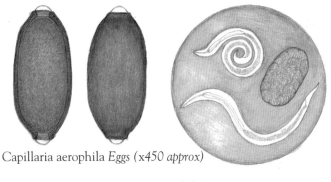

Capillaria aerophila *Eggs* (x450 *approx*)

Crenosoma
striatum
*Larvae and
egg case*
(x225 *approx*)

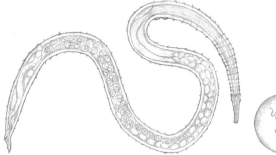

C. striatum *Female with egg cases and larvae inside* (x15 *approx*)

C. striatum *Adults* (*actual size approx*)

Lung worms

Eggs of Capillaria aerophila have a thick, 3-layered shell. Hedgehogs cough up and swallow the eggs of this lung worm, which causes bronchitis and pneumonia.

Larvae of lung worm Crenosoma striatum, a major killer of hedgehogs, are also coughed up and swallowed. Adult females give birth to first-stage larvae. The intermediate hosts are various land snails.

Check saliva and dropping samples under a microscope. Adult worms will only be seen in samples after a hedgehog has been treated with a wormer.

INTERNAL PARASITES

Hedgehogs are prone to infestation by a variety of internal parasites, including lung worm, intestinal nematodes, tapeworms, and flukes. Check the droppings of all hedgehogs for the presence of worm eggs, whether they are showing any symptoms or not. The droppings can appear normal even when the animal has a heavy worm burden.

Intestinal worms and lung worms

Stools with olive or emerald-green mucus, pink flesh, or white stringy pieces indicate intestinal worms, as does diarrhoea with an unpleasant decomposing smell. A thin hedgehog with runny droppings probably needs worming. Treat severe infestations at once with hedgehog-friendly drugs, such as fenbendazole and levamisole (see also p.98).

Threadworms (*Capillaria* sp.) are the commonest nematode detected in hedgehogs' intestines. The damage caused by these parasites invites secondary bacterial infection, producing enteritis, which can be fatal. Affected animals are often thin and undernourished. Two types of lung worm are commonly found in hedgehogs: *Crenasoma striatum* and *Capillaria aerophila* (lung thread worm). Infested animals are likely to be thin and coughing with a runny nose, and particularly vulnerable to pneumonia. Treat with fenbendazole, levamisole, or mebenvet, and give bisolven to dissolve mucus and as an expectorant (see p.104).

Tapeworms

Because it rarely produces symptoms, a tapeworm is hard to detect yet is is often fatal. Diarrhoea may be one sign. Small, whitish segments of the worm shed in the stools are another. If a hedgehog looks thin and in poor condition, suspect tapeworm. As a matter of course, treat all autumn orphans for tapeworm because they are likely to be infested.

Flukes

Eggs may be seen in droppings viewed under a microscope (although eggs are not always in the droppings when a hedgehog is infested). They will kill a hedgehog if left untreated. Symptoms to watch for are loss of appetite with accompanying weight loss, diarrhoea (often containing blood or undigested food), restlessness, and anaemia.

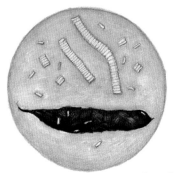

Tapeworm segments and stool

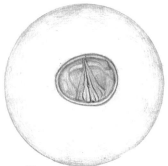

Tapeworm egg

Segments (x 0.75) and egg (x225 approx) from tapeworm Hymenolepis erinacei may be found around stools. Treat with an anthelmintic such as fenbendazole, especially if the hog is restless or losing weight. Various insects act as intermediate host.

79

Homeopathic Treatments

No set homeopathic treatment formula works for all internal parasites. Yet because it is particularly difficult to treat hedgehogs showing no apparent sign of worms (there is little to go on as a guide to the best remedy), the treatment guidelines are not as specific as those for external parasites. However, it is vital that internal parasites are dealt with quickly and efficiently before they get the chance to proliferate and cause more damage. If you are unsure, it is better to treat for the parasites anyway: as long as you use hedgehog-friendly drugs along with homeopathic remedies, you will not harm the hedgehog. (For information on suitable hedgehog-friendly drugs for treating parasites, see Hedgehog Charts, p.104.)

The following is a suggested regime for dealing with internal parasites homeopathically:

For very mild cases or as a prophylactic to build up resistance to parasites, give Sulphur 30c once a week for at least three doses. Hedgehogs due to be released back into the wild (see pp.62-4) will also benefit from this. The Sulphur will help them rid their systems of toxins and build up resistance to parasites.

For moderate infestation, give Sulphur 30c twice daily for 3 to 5 days (depending on severity and the animal's response), then one dose each week for a minimum of three doses.

A heavy infestation will kill a hedgehog unless its parasite burden is reduced rapidly. Only very skilled homeopathic prescribing will prevent you resorting to veterinary drugs to clear the parasites. Give Sulphur 6c twice daily for as long as the drugs are given and continue afterwards with a course of Sulphur 30c once each week for three doses. In addition to building up resistance to the parasites, the Sulphur will help the animal cope with the drugs better.

The following are often helpful for internal parasites: Calc carb, Cina, Filix mas, Graphites, and Spigelia. If Calc carb is indicated by your hedgehog's symptoms, give this first in at least a 30c potency and repeat dosage as for Sulphur. Do not give Sulphur straight after Calc because it is antidotal. Graphites can be given instead of Sulphur, if better indicated by the hedgehog's condition. Cina and Filix mas work best when given in a mother tincture (the undiluted remedy) or in a very

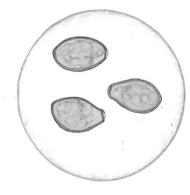

Eggs (x480 approx)

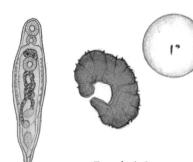

Female (x8 approx) Coiled female (x8 approx) Flukes (actual size)

Brachylaemus *fluke eggs (top) may be seen in stools. Flukes (females in centre and right) should be treated with fenbendazole or medendazole, plus a vitamin supplement (with B complex) to prevent anaemia. Land snails act as intermediate hosts.*

80

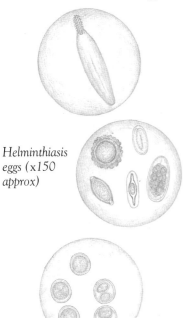

*Acanthocephala
(x5 approx)*

*Helminthiasis
eggs (x150
approx)*

Isospora (x300 approx)

*Little is known about some
parasites found in stools,
such as the thorny-headed
worm (top) and helminthiasis eggs (middle). More is
known about protozoa, such
as* Isospora *(bottom) and*
Cryptosporidia. *These can
cause coccidiosis –
symptoms include loss of
appetite and watery, blood-
stained droppings.*

low potency, such as 1x, 3x, or 6x. Cina is especially good for ascarids, and Filix mas for tapeworms. They can be given in addition to one of the above remedies. Give twice a day for a few days, or until the hedge-hog responds, then stop. Give another dose at weekly intervals for at least one month.

Spigelia is good for all kinds of worms. Use a 3x potency twice daily until the hedgehog responds, then one dose a week for a month. Spigelia is particularly indicated where there is colic from the worms, and lumps of mucus passed in droppings. Spigelia works particularly well alongside Calc, as it is complementary to it.

For lung worm, the same guidelines apply as for other worms. Sulphur has a particularly good record – most hedgehogs will stop coughing straight away after a dose of Sulphur (if lung worm is the cause of the cough). Watch out for signs of pneumonia, which is often a com-plication of lung worm damage. Be suspicious of any hedgehog with a runny nose or with breathing difficulties. Always ask the vet to listen to its chest with a stethoscope and give a diagnosis. Lung worm must be treated with an anthelminthic or it will be fatal (in the case of *Crenosoma*, death could happen with few symptoms).

Severe infestation of internal parasites brings a high risk of sec-ondary bacterial infection developing in the intestines, most commonly E. coli or occasionally Salmonella. If this is likely or you spot any symp-toms which may suggest this (see E. coli in the Materia Medica, p.103), give a dose of the appropriate nosode in a 30c potency at once. Follow this with whichever remedies are indicated by the symptoms. The nosode will help to prevent the infection developing, if it is about to, and help the hedgehog overcome any infection already present (see Resources, p.98).

Finally, there is a combination remedy (one made up of several remedies) which is good for clearing all parasites. You will only be able to obtain this from a homeopathic pharmacy or a homeopath (ask for Powell remedy P55). Give it with whichever specific remedy is best indicated by the hedgehog's general state. Give one tablet three times daily for a minimum of two weeks. This remedy contains both Filix mas and Spigelia, so you will not need to give either of these separately.

CHAPTER FOUR

Other Complementary Therapies

Although homeopathy is the principal complementary therapy the WHH uses to treat hedgehogs, there are several others that are both safe and successful. This chapter deals with the most helpful of these healing alternatives.

Crystal Healing

The healing properties of crystals and gemstones have been known about and made use of for centuries and throughout the world. This section deals with those stones that are the most helpful to hedgehogs. The list is by no means complete, as we are still learning about the many different stones and their potential uses.

What is particularly interesting is that the hedgehogs seem to sense when a crystal is good for them. They will lie with it, lick it, or carry it around with them. They also seem to know when they have had enough from the crystal, and so move away from it. It is hard to know whether or not this is just coincidence, but since many animals seek out particular plants with therapeutic properties, why not crystals?

Before using any crystal you will need to cleanse it in order to get the best from it. Soaking it overnight in a solution of salt water will be sufficient (sea water or sea salt dissolved in spring water is best). You can also use the creative visualization technique (see p.89), substituting the crystal for the hedgehog. Placing the crystal on a purple plate (see p.90) for half an hour or so will cleanse it and re-energise it. This cleansing process needs to be repeated frequently to allow the crystal to work efficiently, since it absorbs negative energies from the sick hedgehog. The sicker the hedgehog, the more often you will need to cleanse

The rose quartz crystal, or Love Stone, is a great comfort to orphaned hedgehogs. At the WHH, orphans are given one to curl up with. It helps to heal grief and other emotional problems.

After she was hit by a car, Hogerty (right) suffered severe head injuries and meningitis. She was saved by treating her with crystals, homeopathy, and healing.

the crystals you use. If the crystal goes dull or sticky, or loses any of its rainbows, it needs cleansing.

You can use as many crystals as you like with your hedgehog. Make sure the crystals used are both large enough, so the hedgehog doesn't eat them, and have no sharp edges. Just put the crystal in the sleeping quarters of the hedgehog's pen. If the hedgehog is asleep or unconscious, put the crystal beside it and in as close contact as possible. Hedgehogs tend to mess up their pens very quickly so the crystal will need cleaning frequently. When changing the hedgehog's bedding, don't throw out the crystal by mistake. To avoid such problems, suspend the crystal from the roof of the pen, either on its own, in lace, or in a mesh bag. This is fine for an active hedgehog who will, by investigating the crystal, lick or nibble at it.

The following crystals are the most useful in hedgehog care:

Agate: This grounding stone is particularly useful for hedgehogs that are unconscious or in a coma. It helps to bring them back fully into their bodies and return to consciousness.

Amethyst: Because this crystal has a soothing, tranquilizing effect, it is very good for hedgehogs that are stressed, nervous, and fearful. It also helps to detoxify the body, as well as stimulate the immune system, the production of red blood cells, and tissue regeneration.

Dioptase: An all-round healer with a particular affinity for all animals, dioptase relaxes the mind and strengthens the central nervous system. It helps the cardiovascular system, so give this stone to any hedgehog that is stressed or suffering from heart problems.

Onyx: Pale green onyx is the colour used at the WHH. It calms the emotions (bringing balance to a stressed animal) and strengthens bone marrow (so give to any hedgehog with bone injuries).

Quartz, Clear: All long-term inmates at the WHH are given a clear quartz crystal. This stone is useful for healing all manner of physical ailments because it helps alleviate emotional stress, and enhances tissue regeneration. Clear quartz can act in various ways: focusing, transforming, amplifying, or storing energy. It also enhances the effects of any other crystals used with it and can be used to purify drinking water, by leaving a crystal to soak in the water overnight.

Quartz, Rose: see page 82.

84

Ruby: Unpolished ruby, which you can buy quite cheaply, strengthens the immune system and aids circulation and tissue regeneration. It is particularly good for the heart.

Other crystals: The following crystals have all been found helpful at the WHH: Amber, Fluorite, Jade, Lapis Lazuli, Sodalite, Bloodstone, Jasper, Rhodonite, Rhodochrosite, Moonstone, Aventurine, Bornite, Citrine, Garnet, Jet, Labradorite, Smoky Quartz, Sugalite, Tiger's Eye, and Topaz.

Bach Flower Remedies

These simple flower essences work, like homeopathy, on the body's energy field, or aura. However, they are not to be confused with homeopathic remedies, which act in a different way and require very different methods of administration. Bach flower remedies infuse the patient's aura with the positive energy from a particular flower. This infusion brings about subtle positive changes in the mind, spirit, and emotions of the patient, which in turn can benefit the physical body if used alongside other treatments.

Bach flower remedies are very safe for hedgehogs because there are no side-effects. The remedies should be administered in a diluted form. Put two drops of the selected remedy in a 30ml medicine bottle containing three quarters spring water and one quarter alcohol (as pure as possible) or cider vinegar. The alcohol or vinegar preserves the mixture, and is not necessary if you are likely to use all of the mixture in a day or two. If you don't have a bottle available just put the dose in a cup of water; this will only keep for a day. When not in use, keep the mixture out of sunlight in a cool place, preferably in the refrigerator.

For hedgehogs, the dose is two drops of the solution three to four times daily, or as indicated. In an acute situation, you may need to give a remedy more frequently, e.g. every 15 minutes, until the hedgehog's condition has improved. The dose is best given by mouth, as with homeopathic remedies. If this is not possible, put the drops on a clean patch of the hedgehog's skin, or in a small quantity of food or drink.

Continue with the daily dose until the hedgehog has improved, usually within about 10 days in chronic cases if the animal is going to respond. Acutely ill animals will show a response within a few hours.

You will not do any harm by carrying on longer than is absolutely necessary. You can give one remedy at a time or a mixture of several. Put two drops of each remedy in the medicine bottle and administer as for single remedies. In the case of Rescue Remedy, put four drops from the stock bottle into your mixture.

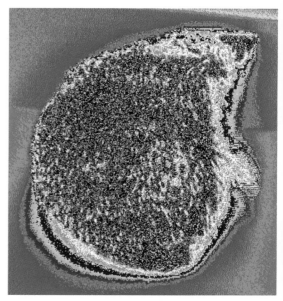

To get the best from the 38 Bach flower essences, study them all to see which ones are best suited to your hedgehog. At the WHH, only a few of these remedies have been used and these are all listed below. Bach flower remedies are compatible with all the other treatments mentioned in this book and with conventional veterinary drugs.

Rescue Remedy: If you have only one flower essence this is the one to have. Made up of five different flower remedies – Cherry Plum, Clematis, Impatiens, Rock Rose, and Star of Bethlehem – Rescue Remedy is useful for shock and all kinds of emergencies. Animals respond to it very well. Use it where a hedgehog has undergone any sort of trauma or is distressed. Applied externally in solution, Rescue Remedy can also be useful on cuts, wounds, and skin ailments.

This image shows the multi-coloured energetic field, or aura, of Pip, a healthy young hedgehog born and reared at the WHH. The technique used to capture this image is called Polycontrast Image Processing (P.I.P), pioneered by Harry Oldfield of the School of Electro-Crystal Therapy.

Crab Apple: This flower remedy is excellent for cleansing and detoxifying the body. Use Crab Apple to help hedgehogs overcome infections, skin disorders, or parasites, and to help rid the body of the ill-effects from drugs. Applied in solution to the affected area, Crab Apple can help to combat skin disorders and external parasites. Before releasing them, give all hedgehogs a course of Crab Apple for a week or two to make sure they go back to the wild cleansed and energized, and with increased resistance to parasites.

Impatiens: Irritable, nervous hedgehogs that are easily stressed will be helped by this remedy. Bad-tempered hedgehogs that snort at the slightest irritation or disturbance are likely to need Impatiens.

Mimulus: Useful for shy, timid hedgehogs who are easily frightened and very sensitive to noise and any other stress.

Olive: Invaluable for exhaustion, whether mental or physical, olive is good for hedgehogs that have collapsed or are starving, or that have come in weak and exhausted after struggling with illness or injury.

Rock Rose: Given after any fright, whether recent or not, Rock Rose releases the remaining tension and panic. Good to give hedgehogs before and after going to the vet, or undergoing any stressful treatment.

Star of Bethlehem: Very helpful for healing the effects of any kind of trauma, whether recent or not. It reintegrates and balances the aura, and is particularly beneficial to orphans and other hedgehogs who have experienced loss, and to accident victims.

Sweet Chestnut: For hedgehogs which seem to have given up and for cases that seem hopeless. Particularly helpful to orphans, hedgehogs with very serious injuries or illness, and hedgehogs in a state of collapse.

Walnut: Particularly useful in times of transition, Walnut helps with adjustment to a change in circumstance. It could therefore be said to be indicated in all hedgehogs that are unfortunate enough to be in captivity. I would certainly recommend giving it to any hedgehogs that seem particularly stressed by their environment or circumstances. It would also benefit hedgehogs undergoing rehabilitation into the wild – so give Walnut for a week or so before the animal's release.

Colour Therapy

The use of different colours has proved very helpful for a number of hedgehog problems. Hedgehogs are not colour blind as was once supposed, and are likely to distinguish between certain colours. However, it is not necessary for a hedgehog to be able to perceive a colour for the colour to have a beneficial effect.

You can use colour therapy on your hedgehog in various ways. Put a light bulb of the appropriate colour in a lamp and shine the light over the hedgehog's pen. Alternatively, you can use different colour filters on ordinary light bulbs. The hedgehog is likely to move away from the light source when it has had enough. Another method involves putting spring or filtered water in a bottle of the required colour and leaving it in sunlight for a few hours. Then give the water to the hedgehog to drink, or bathe him with it, depending on the hedgehog's requirements. If you give healing (see pp.88-90), you can visualize the appropriate colour(s) around the hedgehog. The fol-

Teddy, who has white breast fur and a dark coat like an East European hedgehog, was hyperactive and refused to eat. He was saved by healing and homeopathy.

lowing colours have been particularly beneficial at the WHH:

Blue: A colour very much associated with healing. Useful for fevers and inflammation, and for soothing pain.

Green: A calming colour, green is good for babies and for heart problems, for aiding the nervous system and easing muscle spasms.

Indigo: Excellent for hedgehogs with breathing difficulties, including pneumonia, indigo will also calm hyperactivity. Indigo light is very popular since hedgehogs that are ill like to bathe in it.

Infra-red and Ultra-violet: Although these lights can be used in veterinary treatment of animals, they are very powerful and can be damaging if the hedgehog has too much of them. Use other, safer colours.

Orange: A stimulating colour, orange is good for hedgehogs that are fearful or depressed, or generally lacking in energy.

Peach: A mild painkiller, peach is good for hedgehogs in pain.

Pink: The colour associated with unconditional love, pink is particularly good for orphans or for any hedgehog that has experienced loss.

Red: A very stimulating, energizing colour which is good for the circulation, for clearing negative energies, and for healing arthritis. Give to hedgehogs that are either lacking in vitality or are anaemic. Red is a powerful colour, so only use it for short periods.

Silver: A very cleansing colour, silver is particularly good for helping hedgehogs overcome bacterial or viral infections.

Violet: A good colour for combatting viruses, violet strengthens the nervous and immune systems, and combats fatigue and stress.

Yellow: This purifying colour is good for hedgehogs that are toxic. Lemon yellow is especially good for helping to combat parasitic infestations. In addition to using yellow light, you could use lemon yellow water for bathing wounds or areas of infected skin, or spray over areas infested with external parasites.

Healing

Healing works directly on the hedgehog's energy field, or aura, to bring balance and improve health. Every living thing has an energy body which surrounds and interpenetrates the physical body. This has been seen by healers and psychics for many years, and now scientists are beginning to work with this energy field and find ways to record it. The energy field, or aura (see p.86), is like a blueprint of what is taking place in the physical body. By working to correct imbalances and damage in the aura the physical body can also be healed. You do not need to be a trained healer to help your hedgehog in this way. Make sure you are in a relaxed and positive frame of mind, and your hedgehog will be more relaxed in response. This is the only way to give healing successfully, otherwise you would transmit your negative state to the hedgehog.

There are three simple techniques you can try. The first is creative visualization. Imagine a gold light glowing within the centre of your hedgehog. This could be a star, a candle flame, or whatever works best for you. Focus on the light and allow it grow, expand, and become brighter, filling the hedgehog's body. Allow it to expand a little beyond the animal's physical body until your hedgehog is immersed in a glowing ball of gold light. Hold this image for as long as feels appropriate, even a few seconds is helpful (you may find your hedgehog knows when it's had enough and begins to move away!). You can repeat this exercise as often as you like, it will only do good.

The next technique involves giving healing more directly. In a relaxed and balanced state, imagine healing energy or light streaming into you through the top of your head. At the same time, imagine roots going down through the soles of your feet into the earth. Feel the earth energy coming up through these roots into your body. Allow the energy from above and below to flow through your body and reach your heart chakra in the centre of your chest. From here, let the energy flow into your arms and out through your hands. Put your hands either directly on your hedgehog or as close to the animal as feels comfortable for you both. Visualize the healing energy flowing out of your hands into the body of the hedgehog.

As you do this, move your hands around the hedgehog and feel around the area an inch or two outside its physical body. See if you can feel or see any area which needs special attention – this could feel like a hole in the energy field or a place that feels denser than the rest. When you find such an area, allow your hands to remain there, focusing the healing energy until you feel a change. Continue in this way until you have covered the whole of the hedgehog's physical body and aura. To finish off, gently stroke just above and around the hedgehog from front to back, smoothing out the aura. Make sure it feels balanced equally on both sides of the hedgehog's body. If it seems to be more to one side, gently move the energy across until it is central. Now step back from the hedgehog and imagine yourself closing off the top of your head and the soles of your feet, stopping the healing energy. This exercise should make you feel good as well as your hedgehog!

The last technique is a simple way to send absent healing when you cannot be there to do it directly. Again, make sure you are relaxed before you start. Either imagine yourself being with the hedgehog or imagine it in the room with you, whichever works best for you. Imagine placing your hands on the hedgehog and use one of the above two healing techniques. As you finish, either put the hedgehog back or bring yourself back, so you are both in the right place!

Use these exercises as often as you like and for all physical, emotional or mental ailments, especially if you are unsure which remedy to give. Healing complements homeopathy and the other treatments in this book, including conventional veterinary drugs. If you are stuck with a case or are unsure about giving healing yourself, turn to the contact list (see Resources) to find a healer near you.

Purple Plates

The positive energy plate, or purple plate, is an extraordinarily powerful healing tool. It is made from aluminium which has been treated specially to enable it to act as a transceiver of universal energy. Purple plates increase energy and relieve pain, and have either a stimulating or soothing effect, depending on what is needed. Hedgehogs, no matter what their size, often go and lie on the plate, and move off when its work is done. It is of great help in emergencies, often reviving unconscious hedgehogs. Put seriously ill hedgehogs on the plate when giving first aid or fluids, or whilst working out which remedy to give.

Aromatherapy

Essential oils can be used in burners, pans, joss-sticks, and pomanders to infuse the air with a particular oil. They can also be used in baths (just a few drops), or inhaled with steam. The oils, when infused into the air of a room, can calm hedgehogs, overcome unpleasant smells, positively charge the ions in the air, and kill bacteria and viruses. Some oils (camphor, menthol, eucalyptus, and peppermint), because of their particularly strong smells, are antidotal to homeopathic remedies. Keep these oils well away from your remedy store and don't use any that are antidotal on or around hedgehogs receiving homeopathic treatment. The following oils are the most frequently used at the WHH:

Eucalyptus: For breathing troubles. Antidotal.

Olbas oil: For breathing troubles. Antidotal.

Lavender: The most commonly used oil. It has a calming, balancing effect, and is a natural insect repellent. It soothes pain and inflammation, is antiseptic, kills bacteria, and helps to expel parasites.

Tea Tree, or **Ti Tree:**   An antiviral, antifungal, antibacterial, and antiparasitic oil. It strengthens the immune system, thereby increasing the hedgehog's natural resistance to disease.

Rosemary: Stimulates the brain and central nervous system. A general tonic and painkiller that helps clear catarrh and breathing problems.

Natural Smells and Soothing Sounds

Hedgehogs can benefit from exposure to some of the natural smells they miss in captivity. Since their sense of smell is so important in finding their way about and seeking prey, it must be disorientating to be without familiar smells. Pieces of bark, wood, grass, leaves, or wild flowers placed in a hedgehog's house make them feel more at home.

Hedgehogs rely heavily on their hearing and so are very responsive to sound. The following have had a beneficial effect: Johann Strauss waltzes, Pachalbel's Canon, Enya, European bird song, and natural environment noise. Choose calm, gentle, flowing sounds. Try to keep your hedgehogs somewhere quiet, and play any music quietly. Sounds to avoid are: Mozart (too powerful and jumpy), rock music (especially heavy metal), sounds of predatory animals, and jungle noises.

Appendices

&

Hedgehog Case Histories

Hattie

When Hattie arrived with compound fractures of both front legs, we gave her Arnica 200c to help her cope with the gas and antibiotics she needed. The vet put a plastic splint made from a syringe case on one leg and sprayed it with antibiotic. One leg swelled up and turned septic. This recurred, bringing abscess after abscess. Her wounds suppurated all the time, leaving a pool of pus wherever she went. The Silica 30c and other remedies we gave her reduced the swelling and localized the suppuration. However, her leg may have to be amputated. Most recently, Hattie has received healing, which has brought about a further improvement. Her progress contrasts sharply with that of Zorba (see p.45), who received homeopathic treatment but no gas and antibiotics. Zorba's recovery, from equally severe injuries, was much speedier, with no abscesses, and is typical of cases treated homeopathically.

Pebbles

Pebbles looked dead on arrival at the WHH. She had been hit by a car, apparently, then thrown over a hedge. She was ice cold and had stopped breathing. Jane detected a very faint heartbeat and gave Pebbles Carbo veg 200c and Aconite 200c until she started breathing properly. She was tube fed at first, but soon she was fully conscious and able to suck from a syringe.

Both her hind legs had compound fractures near the hips. The bones stuck through the wounds, which were badly infected, and full of foul-smelling pus. She was too weak for an operation and her legs too infected for the bones to be pinned or splinted. A single antibiotic injection was followed by Arnica, Symphytum, and other first-aid remedies, and healing with the colour blue every day for two weeks. Her wounds were bathed with Calendula and salt water, and kept open to drain. She was put on veterinary pads or disposable nappies to soak up the pus, and kept in a small pen to restrict her movement. She made a remarkable recovery. Her bones healed naturally and the infection cleared up without recurrence. As well as walking, she can stand on three legs and scratch with her fourth!

Bubbles

After being hit by a car, Bubbles was left with one eye, a fractured skull, and a punctured lung, which made him fill with air like a balloon and unable to move. The vet released the air with a hypodermic and gave him antibiotics and liquid food. A week later, a piece of skin came away from his back because it had no circulation when he was inflated – since this left him unable to curl up, he was kept as a resident of the WHH.

During his first winter, he tried to hibernate but he was found cold and lifeless with laboured breathing (he needed to curl up to hibernate). He was slowly warmed with a water bottle, then given Lectade. It took him 24 hours to recover. When he tried to hibernate the next year, he was given Aconite 30 regularly and a heated pad. He took about half the time to recover, without discomfort. He lived until he was 7 years of age.

Ollie

Ollie came in covered in tar, which had sealed her mouth and eyes. We cleaned her with Swarfega and diluted washing-up liquid, paying particular attention to her eyes and mouth. We gave her Gelsemium 30c for the shock and to stimulate her appetite. Ollie passed black oily droppings, so she'd obviously swallowed a lot of tar, too. We gave her Petroleum 30c to help clear this, and fed her charcoal and kaolin to help her digestion. After a full recovery, she was released at a safe site.

Hedgie

After falling and paralysing herself from the waist down, Hedgie could only drag her hind legs. She responded to Conium, but it took two weeks to show any improvement in her legs. She received Conium 30c twice daily for a week, then one dose every three days, then once a week, and finally once a month until she was fully recovered.

Puddles

Puddles was an 8-week-old juvenile found trapped in a breeze block with water and cow dung. She was wet, weak, starving, caked in cow dung, and covered in hundreds of maggots. Her claws were worn down as she had scratched to get out, and her knuckles were bleeding. With warm salt water, we painstakingly removed the dung and flushed out the maggots. Then we gave her Assissi eye drops and veterinary ear drops.

She drank Lectade and lots of fluids. Puddles refused dog food and would only eat her natural diet: live insects (bought from breeders, so free of parasites) supplemented with dried insect food, slippery elm, and Esbilac. She was given Aconite 200c initially, followed by Sulphur 30c, each repeated as needed. Puddles grew up to be a fine adult and was released.

Jasper

Jasper arrived at the WHH with severe mange. He showed a typical Sulphur symptom picture: active, thin, smelly, and dirty with hot skin but a good appetite. He had a cough, due to internal worms, and was very thirsty. He was covered in mite, which had caused him to lose most of his spines and hair; his skin was flaky. He was dehydrated, wobbly, and very thin. Jasper was given Panacur wormer and Sulphur 30c in repeated doses. He also had healing from the Harry Edwards Spiritual Healing Sanctuary. For his mite, we gave him herbal baths (containing garlic juice, herb Robert, and elder leaves) and garlic baths. He was given vitamin and mineral supplements and his pen and bedding cleaned frequently. Jasper is now putting on weight, his hair and spines have grown back, but he still has some ringworm.

Amethyst

Amethyst was one of three female orphans who were found very weak and starving. The largest had to be euthanased (she was given Arnica 200c first) by the vet as her intestines had prolapsed and her sisters had pulled her gut out further and nibbled at it. We gave the other two Aconite 200c but Amethyst's smallest sister died within 24 hours. The post mortem showed emaciation and cachexia to be the cause of death, and the little hog had no fat left in her body.

It looked as if Amethyst might die, too. She refused to eat or drink after her sister died and lost weight rapidly. Jane gave her Ignatia 200c, a teddy bear, an amethyst crystal and a mini purple plate, which she carried everywhere. (Amethyst was named after this crystal which she liked to carry around, along with her purple plate!)

Jane force-fed her on fluids and liquidized food for a couple of weeks, which kept her alive. Lab results on her droppings showed several parasitic problems: cryptosporidia, haemolytic and non-haemolytic E. coli and another organism. Then she received absent healing from the Harry Edwards Spiritual Healing Sanctuary and made an instant improvement. She continued to receive healing for three months. She recovered completely and is now full grown and ready for release.

RSPCA Cases

The RSPCA's Wildlife Hospital at West Hatch, Somerset, has been using homeopathy under veterinary advice for many years. Here are two of their case histories.

An adult male with fractures of the tibia and fibula in one leg was given Hypericum 30c daily for six days and Symphytum daily for 10 days. The leg was splinted and he soon made a complete recovery and was released.

A group of 11- to 12-day-old babies, whose eyes were still unopened, were brought in after people had disturbed the nest and placed the babies in a field, thinking the mother would return. The babies were clearly distressed and squealed continually, until they were given Ignatia 30c. Within a few hours, they had all fallen fast asleep. They continued to thrive and were released when they were old enough.

Hedgehog Repertory

Use this section to help you and your vet tackle hedgehog problems homeopathically (see also Chapter Two for general care). The suggestions for remedies and dosages are only meant as a guide – they may not be right for your hedgehog. Always be guided by the symptoms of a particular case and the response of the hedgehog. Use the Materia Medica (see pp.99-103) to check how well the suggested remedies match the symptoms.

Amputation

Partially or wholly severed limbs are common but sometimes damage is so severe that amputation is necessary. A vet will need to do this. For immediate care after amputation give Hypericum to help with nerve pains and to prevent infection. Otherwise, treat as for fractures. Problems often recur in the stumps, where abscesses may develop. Ledum is good for irritable stumps, and Hepar or Silica for infected stumps.

Anaesthetics (to be administered only by a vet)

To lessen the shock of an anaesthetic and to enable the hedgehog to process it better, give Arnica 200c before and immediately after the anaesthetic is administered. If 200c is unavailable, give the next highest potency you can. The Arnica will help the hedgehog to come round. But if an animal still has problems overcoming the anaesthetic, give Phosphorus 30c and repeat as needed.

Bruising

Arnica is best for all soft tissue bruising and Ruta for bruised bone and fibrous tissue. Give Arnica 30c twice a day for 3 days or until the most acute swelling and bruising dies down. Carry on for as long as required with a 6c twice daily. Most soft tissue bruising will be healed within a week. For deeper bruising or where bone is involved give Ruta 6c twice daily for 2 to 3 weeks, or as required. You can give Arnica and Ruta concurrently, but separately, i.e. at least half an hour apart.

Burns

Treat for shock and dehydration as well (esp. if burns are severe). Causticum and Cantharis are the main internal remedies. If the burns are severe, Causticum is indicated. Either remedy takes the pain out of the burns. Repeat when discomfort and pain return; in a severe case, this may be every few hours at first. Carry on giving the remedy as needed until the burn is healed. Help the healing process by treating the burn externally. Clean the lesion and apply a solution either of the same remedy you are giving internally or of Urtica urens (put a drop of the remedy, or crush and dissolve a tablet, in a little warm water). **NB**: Burns can become infected, so always ask your vet to assess them.

Circling

Hedgehogs that run in circles have been cured at the WHH. Most commonly caused by ear mites or an ear infection (when the animal holds its head to one side), or a head injury. Also boredom or lack of space. Newly blind hedgehogs may circle at first. Treatment depends on the cause. Useful remedies are Aconite, Arnica, Calc carb, Causticum, Conium, Gelsemium, and Sulphur. **NB:** Hedgehogs that constantly circle will need more food than usual because they burn it up more rapidly.

Collapse

Carbo veg can often revive a collapsed hedgehog, even when it has stopped breathing. If possible, give at least a 30c potency; 200c is better. Repeat every 10 to 20 mins, until the hedgehog gets stronger. Other remedies are Aconite (esp. when very cold or from heart attack) and Arnica (esp. after physical injury or exhaustion). They all may be needed at different times; if one is not helping try another until you get a response. Get Lectade into the hedgehog as soon as possible and keep it warm, or it will not maintain improvement from the remedies.

Dehydration

Get Lectade to the hedgehog. The most likely remedies to help it respond faster are Aconite, Arsenicum, Calc carb, Carbo veg, China, Phosphorus, and Silica.

Digestive Problems

Appetite, loss of: Aconite is usually successful. Where there are no other symptoms, try Nux vomica. The purple plate may help, too. Try giving live yoghurt or

Complan. Check its mouth for an injury or obstacle.

Constipation: Give live yoghurt or Acidopholus. Make sure the constipation is not caused by food that is too dry. Hedgehogs constipated because of a blockage (e.g. caused by shedding dead worms after wormers) show great discomfort and need urgent veterinary attention. Liquid paraffin or glycerine given orally or syringed up the anus may clear it. For blockages caused by lung worm, inject Bisolven. Useful remedies are Bryonia, Calc carb, Graphites, Lycopodium, Nux vom, Silica, Sulphur, and, in case of complete blockage, Opium. A potency of 30c generally works best.

Diarrhoea: Do not give food to a hedgehog with diarrhoea. Give fluids only (water and Lectade, or glucose and water) for 24 hours to give the animal's intestines a rest. Always treat diarrhoea as very serious in babies. Send a sample of droppings for analysis. Charcoal or kaolin will help bring relief. The nosodes E. coli, Salmonella, or Candida may help, particularly if lab. results show these organisms to be present. Give a single dose of the 30c potency, followed by other indicated remedies. The most common for diarrhoea are Ant tart, Arsenicum, Calc carb (esp. babies), Chamomilla, Colocynth (esp. with colicky pains), Lycopodium, Merc sol, Phosphorus, Pulsatilla, Nux vom, and Sulphur.

Vomiting: Most likely to occur along with diarrhoea and pneumonia. Send a sample for analysis. Do not force feed. Give plenty of fluids. If coupled with constipation or no droppings, look for a blockage (see Constipation). If it continues, get further advice. Useful remedies include Aconite, Arsenicum, Ant tart, Chamomilla, China, Nux vom, Phosphorus, Pulsatilla, and Sulphur.

Drugs, Ill Effects of

After administering a drug, give Sulphur 30c twice a day for 2 to 3 days to help eliminate the toxins. If a drug causes an adverse reaction, or if the action of a remedy is halted by a drug, give Sulphur 30c; repeat as needed. Then give a further dose of the antidoted remedy, if it is still indicated. If the hog does not respond to Sulphur, or, if it seems better indicated, give Nux vom.

Whilst a hedgehog is on a course of drugs, give Sulphur or Nux vom daily in a 6c potency and continue for a few days after the drug is stopped. If the animal is very toxic or has had a lot of drugs, a good course to clear its system is Sulphur 6c each morning with Nux vom 6c each evening for 3 weeks. Homeopathy will not interfere with any positive effects of drugs.

Beneficial bacteria in the gut are destroyed by antibiotics, so replace with live lactobacillus. Also, any *Candida albicans* present may multiply, so give a dose of the Candida nosode 30c to help keep it under control.

Avoid steroids if possible because they stop the action of homeopathic remedies and produce strong side-effects. If they are used, give a dose of steroid in a 30c potency to help the hedgehog to cope with the drug, and follow it with any indicated remedies.

Fractures

Generally require the administration of several remedies concurrently, since each helps with a particular aspect of the injury. As with any physical trauma, give Arnica first – start with a 200c potency and after a few doses change to 6c. This helps with the shock, haemorrhage, and bruising. Ruta helps the pain from bruised bony tissue. To help the fracture heal, give Symphytum 6c twice daily for at least 3 weeks (it takes this long for bone to heal). In compound fractures, bathe the wound and keep it open (see Wounds). The programme I find most useful is: Arnica 200c twice daily for 2 to 3 days, then 6c twice daily for another week. Ruta 6c twice daily for 2 to 3 weeks. Symphytum 6c twice daily for 3 weeks or until break is fully healed.

Gangrene

Very serious and needs urgent veterinary attention. Amputation of the affected limb may be needed to prevent gangrene spreading. Give one of the following: Arsenicum, Cantharis, Carbo veg, Lachesis, or Silica. Pyrogen 30c will help prevent the infection spreading.

Haemorrhage

Try to arrest bleeding (e.g. with artery forceps) then give a dose of the right remedy within a minute or two; repeat dose as needed if the bleeding starts again. The most useful remedies for stopping haemorrhage are Aconite, Arnica, Calendula, China, Ferrum phos, and

Phosphorus. If the animal is weak from loss of blood, give China and Ferrum phos 6x (2 to 3 times a day for 2 weeks) to help return haemoglobin levels to normal.

Head Injuries
Nearly always need Arnica and Aconite. Even old head injuries respond and swellings will reduce. Meningitis can develop after a head injury. Treat fits, coma, or loss of balance as an emergency; contact the vet and give appropriate remedies. Check for lumps, asymmetrical head, and damage to roof of mouth or lower jaw. Fractured skulls usually heal well with no brain damage.

If the animal bleeds from its ears or holds its head on one side, check its hearing by clicking your fingers on each side. Look down the ears with a torch pen to check for damage. Often, the eyes bulge and go cloudy when the brain is inflamed. Eyes are often lost, blinded, or need to be removed after head injuries. Keep eye sockets and wounds clean. Eyes can heal remarkably well. Useful remedies for eyes are Euphrasia, Ledum, Ruta, and Symphytum. **NB**. Concussed hedgehogs can take months to recover fully, so don't release them. Slower reactions or an inability to think clearly make them more vulnerable to attack and accidents.

Heat Stroke/Sunstroke
Most likely to occur in captivity, unless the animal lives in a hot climate. The primary remedy is Belladonna, ideally given in a 200c potency. Other remedies which may be useful for overheated animals are Apis, Bryonia, Pulsatilla, and Sulphur.

Hyperactivity (extreme restlessness)
Most common in orphans and often associated with a heavy internal parasite burden. Can be due to stress. Restlessness usually continues until the animal collapses and dies – so treat as an emergency. Useful remedies are Aconite, Arnica, Arsenicum, Cannabis indica, Ignatia, Nux vom, Sulphur, Tarentula hispanica.

Hypothermia
Aconite is the first remedy, preferably a 200c or at least a 30c potency. The hedgehog should respond quickly, and begin to warm up. Other useful remedies for the effects of cold are Arnica, Arsenicum, Calc carb, China, Carbo veg, Causticum, Ignatia, Phosphorus, and Silica.

Infectious Diseases, Acute
Hepatitis, listeria, meningitis, pneumonia, and Salmonella are some of the most common acute infections to which hedgehogs succumb. Identify the pathogen and give a 30c dose of it. If you or the vet suspect a particular disease, give the nosode (p. 103) because, if it is close enough, it will still be of help. Give remedies as indicated by the symptoms, which may change rapidly.

Parasites
See Chapter Three, pages 73-81.

Poisoning
Take the hedgehog to the vet. Identify the poison and ask a homeopath or pharmacist to make up a 30c potency of the substance. Give this alongside any indicated remedies to help clear the poison from the system. Nux vom and Sulphur are the most useful remedies. If the animal is very weak, keep to low potencies only and repeat them frequently since they will not overtax the eliminatory organs and will enhance their function. Other useful remedies are Aconite, Arnica, Arsenicum, Apis, Belladonna, Bryonia, Causticum, Hepar sulph, Mercurius, Phosphorus, and Pulsatilla.

Respiratory Problems
Breathing difficulties: Can be due to various causes (e.g. nose injury, bronchitis, pneumonia). Check saliva and dropping samples for worm eggs, larvae, and pathogens. Start all cases with Aconite 200c or 30c (if injured, give Arnica, too). For pneumonia and bronchitis, Ant tart 30c, Carbo veg 200c, and Sulphur 30c have all been effective. Other useful remedies are Pulsatilla, Phosphorus, Bryonia, and Silica.
Cough: The most common cause is lung worm, so check saliva and droppings. Sulphur 30c is usually effective. Other remedies are Bryonia and Phosphorus.
Punctured Lung: Makes the hedgehog fill up with gas or air, which needs to be removed. If the circulation to parts of the body is cut off, causing skin to die and

slough away, give Carbo veg. A vet will show you how to deflate the hedgehog using a hypodermic syringe. *Rattling*: Usually due to lung worm or bronchitis. Check droppings and saliva. Use a stethoscope to listen to the hedgehog's chest and take its temperature. Remedies most likely to help are Aconite, Ant tart, Carbo veg, and Sulphur, preferably in a 30c potency.

Shock

Shock is the biggest killer, but homeopathy is equal to it in saving lives. The three main remedies are Aconite, Arnica, and Ignatia. Aconite is indicated for shock from a fright, exposure to cold, or loss of blood. Arnica is also helpful for shock from fright and loss of blood; it is the primary remedy for all shock due to physical trauma (e.g. accidents, operations, exhaustion). Ignatia is primarily for shock due to emotional trauma, loss, or fright (e.g. orphans or animals who have lost a mate). If you are confused or there are various causative factors, here's a homeopathic trick which often helps: give each remedy in rotation until the hedgehog responds. The best potency for acute shock is 200c, unless the hedgehog is very weak or old, in which case give 30c or less.

Skin Problems

Most likely to be due to external parasites (see pp.73-7) or a wound (see Wounds).

Spinal or Neck Injuries

Move the hedgehog as little as possible, or you could do more damage. Often, the spines lie flat from the injured area downwards. Do not give up hope: there have been some remarkable recoveries from this type of injury at the WHH, using homeopathy. If you have to move the animal, carry it on a piece of foam or small inflatable veterinary bed. Pinch its toes to see if there is any feeling. Check that it can empty its bladder. With neck injuries, the head is often to one side or at an angle. Only X-ray if essential, since this adds to the hedgehog's discomfort. An animal with either neck or spinal injuries cannot go back to the wild because it will not be able to curl up properly. Give Arnica 200c and Hypericum (esp. good for nerve damage where there is

loss of feeling). If there is paralysis, give Conium 30c.

Sprains and Dislocations

Rhus tox and Ruta are the main remedies. Give twice a day for a week or two, depending on the response. Muscles heal faster than fibrous tissue (e.g. ligaments), which may need treatment for 3 weeks or more.

Starvation

Give appropriate shock remedy, then easily digestible foods, such as Complan. Follow with either Arsenicum, Calc carb, Ignatia, Nux vom, Phosphorus, Pulsatilla, Silica, or Sulphur. The nosodes Psorinum and Tuberculinum could also be helpful.

Urinary Problems

Give plenty of water for all urinary problems.
Cystitis: The most commonly useful remedy is Cantharis. If this does not help, or is not indicated, try Apis, Arsenicum, Causticum, or Lycopodium.
Retention: Usually responds to Apis mell, preferably 200c, but any potency should work. If gravel or sand is causing a blockage, give Calc carb or Lycopodium. If unresponsive to treatment, ask your vet to empty the bladder artificially. Move the hedgehog very gently because this condition is painful. Sometimes a cold or warm poultice on the bladder area gets things moving.

Wounds

Keep all wounds clean and remove maggots. For surface wounds and lacerated wounds, Calendula is best; for deeper wounds or puncture wounds, use Hypericum. A useful mixture is Hypercal, made from equal parts Calendula and Hypericum. For all puncture wounds, give Ledum or, if already inflamed, Hypericum. If there are abscesses or the wound is already infected, give Silica or Hepar sulph. Silica is best where the wound harbours dirt or debris, since it will help to expel these. Hepar sulph allows pus to be absorbed. For burns, use a solution of Urtica urens (see Burns). Do not apply a mother tincture neat; put a few drops in bathing water. Before bathing the eyes, sterilize the water by boiling. If you do not have a tincture, crush a tablet or put a drop of the potentized remedy in the bathing water.

Drugs and Medicines

The WHH has found these treaments to be safe. Most are available from a vet, pet shop, or chemist. All drugs have side-effects so use natural remedies where possible.

Bacterial Infections *Amoxycillin, Betamox L.A.:* 15mg/kg. (long-acting injection, gives cover over 48 hours). Inject sub/cut. 0.27ml/kg. *Amoxycillin, Clamoxyl:* 7mg/kg. Inject sub/cut. 0.27ml/kg for 3 to 5 days. *Amoxycillin, Clamoxyl* palatable drops: 5-10mg/kg. Oral 0.25ml/kg. Twice daily for five days. Suitable for babies (they like the taste of this!). *Amoxycillin, Clamoxyl* tablets: 40mg. 0.25 of a tablet twice daily for one week.

Give these injections under supervision of a vet. Do not use stronger antibiotics unless necessary. Never use antibiotics indiscriminately. Send dropping, pus, or saliva samples to a lab. before treatment. At the WHH, we have found that 50% of haemolytic E. coli, 30% of non-haemolytic E. coli, and most haemolytic staphylococcus infections are resistant to amoxycillin.

Protozoa (coccidiosis, including cryptosporidia) *Bimastat* (a sulphonamide-antibiotic combination in a balanced solution of electrolytes includes neomycin, sulphadimidine, sulphathiazole and kaolin): 1.5ml/kg oral for 5 days. *Neo-sulphentrin* suspension (neomycin, streptomycin, sulphathiaz, sulphaguanide): 1.2ml/kg, oral for 5 days. *Sulphonamides:* Only give if absolutely necessary. Others can be used at your vet's discretion.

Wounds *Alamycin* aerosol (contains oxytetracycline and gentian violet): antibiotic spray. *Aureomycin* powder 2% (contains chlortetracycline): antibiotic wound powder. *Dermisol* multicleanse solution: aids removal of necrotic tissue and debris; has antibacterial action. Also as ointment. *Salt water* (1tsp in 500ml) to clean wounds. *Sudocrem:* antiseptic cream for minor wounds. *Vaseline* for sore skin in orphans after toileting. **To stop self-biting of wounds** *Terra-cortril* spray (contains oxytetracycline and hydrocortisone, which is a steroid).

Respiratory problems *Bisolven* injection: sub/cut. 0.25ml/kg twice daily for 5 to 7 days or more. *Bisolven* powder: oral, one pinch daily over 14 days. Olbas oil or other essential oils as inhalers.

Sore throats *Glycerin* BP.

Digestive problems *Probiotic* (Protexin soluble): Sprinkle a little on food daily. *Can-addase:* enzyme supplement, one pinch on food daily. *Laxative* (e.g. castor oil). **Diarrhoea** *Charcoal* or *kaolin*. **Flatulence or stomachache** (esp. babies) Gripe water. **Constipation** *Glycerin* BP or liquid paraffin (but avoid prolonged use).

Dehydration *Lectade:* 1 to 9 warm water; by syringe to mouth or via stomach tube. *Dextrose saline* or *Hartmanns solution:* sub/cut., 50ml/kg daily warmed, add 10% Duphalyte. In severe cases, give intra-peritoneally. *Glucose* powder: one pinch in syringe full of warm water; orally for minor cases.

Ear Infection: *Gac* drops (contain neomycin). One drop in ear twice daily. Wax and mites: *Otodex* or *Assissi* ear drops. **Eye** Infections: *Chloromycetin:* ointment, 5-6 times daily. *Orbenin* ointment. Cleaning: *Optrex* eye drops. *Assissi* eye drops. **Nose** Dab clean with distilled witchhazel. **Mouth** *Dettol Mouth Wash* (not Dettol): 2.5ml in 200ml water. *Salt water* solution.

Parasites (see pp.73-81) **Maggots** *Salt water* and small dental water-jet. **Fleas** *Pyrethrum* powder. **Ringworm** *Garlic* juice. **Ticks** Pluck off and apply Nelsons *pyrethrum* spray to wound or use Hypercal lotion. **Mites** Bath in 0.6% *Alugan* solution every 2-weeks.

External oil or tar Bathe in *washing up liquid* solution. Absorb oil with *Fullers earth* powder. Use *Swarfega.*

Vitamins *Abidec:* multivitamin drops for babies in milk daily 0.5ml/kg. *Vetamin + zinc:* one pinch daily (not suitable for continuous use).

Tranquillizers Use homeopathic remedies only.

Anaesthetic To be given only by a vet. *Halothane:* inhalation. 2-4% in transport medium of oxygen. *Ketamine:* int/musc. 20mg/kg (0.2ml/kg).

Hedgehog Materia Medica

This section is designed to help you select a remedy for your ailing hedgehog. First, assess the animal (see Chapter Two) and then note its symptoms, forming a picture of its condition. Now look up all its problems in the Repertory and note all the remedies listed under each symptom or problem. If you find a remedy is indicated for several problems, it is very likely to be the best choice. Use the information on the remedy in this Materia Medica to confirm the remedy picture does match that of your hedgehog. If no single remedy is apparent, look up all the remedies you have listed from the Repertory and see which fits your hedgehog best.

Each remedy picture shows the main symptoms it can produce and therefore cure. To help you differentiate between remedies, the symptoms have been given two different gradings. In italics, you will find *guiding symptoms* – symptoms particularly characteristic of the remedy. In ordinary type, you will find common symptoms – these are also characteristic of the remedy but to a lesser degree. In order for a remedy to be indicated, your hedgehog should be displaying at least one or two guiding symptoms of that remedy. If no guiding symptoms are present yet some common symptoms are, the remedy is unlikely to be the right one.

All remedies have **modalities.** You can use modalities to help further in distinguishing between different remedies. Modalities show the effects of different stimuli on the patient, i.e. the influences that make the symptoms better (>) or worse (<). For example, in differentiating between Aconite and Arsenicum, which have some guiding symptoms in common, look at their modalities. Aconite has the modality worse (<) at midnight, while Arsenicum has the modality worse after midnight. If your hedgehog appears to need one of these remedies and its condition becomes worse at midnight, then choose Aconite. If the symptoms are worse after midnight, then choose Arsenicum.

Additional information has been provided where relevant, notably what the remedy is particularly useful for and any instructions about how or when to use it.

Aconite

Anxiety, restlessness, fear. Effects of exposure to cold and from fright, particularly when involving a confrontation with death. Haemorrhage of bright red blood. Sudden onset of symptoms. **Modalities**: *< midnight. > fresh air.* **Useful for:** Hypothermia. Shock, esp. from fright or cold. Very useful for weak chilled orphans; will warm them and increase their appetites. Often useful for chest infections, nasal discharge, loss of appetite, breathing difficulties, enteritis. **Instructions for Use:** Give at start of fever or inflammatory states. Give before long examinations or stressful treatments. May need Sulphur or another remedy to follow on and complete the cure.

Antimonium tartaricum (Ant tart)

Weakness, drowsiness, lack of reaction, trembling. Much production of mucus. Rattling in chest. Short, suffocative breathing. Cough loose and rattling. Face sunken and sickly. Blueness of mucous membranes. Eyes dim/full of mucus. Vomiting/diarrhoea. **Modalities**: *< warmth, overheating, anger. > expectoration.* **Useful for:** Mostly for pneumonia and other chest problems, esp. where excess mucus causes rattling and fullness of chest.

Apis mellifica

Painful, hot, oedematous swelling. Puffiness. Redness. Thirstless. Shrieks from pain. Stings. Urinary problems, esp. retention of urine. Meningitis. Panting, as if every breath is the last. Rosy red skin eruptions. Burning heat with no thirst. One part hot, another cold. Bloated fluid filled abdomen. **Modalities:** *< Heat, warm room. << touch. < suppressed discharges. > cool air, cold bathing.*

Arnica

Shock, esp. from physical trauma or fright. Physical injuries. Bruising. Fear of touch or approach. Haemorrhage. Head injuries; concussion; unconsciousness. Restlessness due to discomfort or extreme fatigue. Boils and abscesses. **Modalities**: *< any exertion.* **Useful for:** Any physical injury. Preventing septicaemia. Healing effects of old injuries. **Instructions for Use:** Do not apply externally if skin is broken. Give to mother hedgehog before and after birth. Give before and after surgery or anaesthetic.

Arsenicum album

Restlessness with anxiety, fear. Ill effects of eating bad food. Diarrhoea and acrid discharges, making surrounding area sore. Foul discharges. Thirsty for sips of water. Cold body but head warm. Craves fresh air. Fear of being alone. Not interested in food. Weakness. Falling prickles and hair, flaking skin, mange, dandruff. Itchiness. Watery, acrid, nasal discharge. Haemorrhage of dark blood. Loose, dark, bloody stools. Cystitis with bloody discharge. ***Modalities*** > heat. < after midnight; cold. ***Useful for:*** Very commonly needed for digestive upsets. Esp. suited to fussy, anxious, fastidious types. Calming hyperactive babies. Thin, undernourished hedgehogs. First remedy for thin, restless hedgehogs with digestive problems.

Belladonna

Intense burning heat, esp. the head. Pupils dilated. Redness. Symptoms very violent and come on suddenly. Restless. Has a wild look. ***Modalities:*** *< 3am & 3pm. << touch, jarring, heat, drafts. Symptoms < on right side of body.* ***Useful for:*** Fevers. Sunstroke, effects of overheating. Fits and convulsions. Rapidly brings temperature down.

Bryonia

Heat and dryness. Very irritable. Thirsty for large quantities of water. Stools large, dry and hard. Dry, hard cough. Bronchitis. Prefers to lie on affected part, as pressure relieves. Abscesses. Constipation. ***Modalities:*** *<< Heat. < the least motion; around 9pm. > pressure on painful part; cold things.* ***Useful for:*** Coughs and respiratory problems in hedgehogs that are irritable, i.e. tend to snort and bristle when touched.

Calc carb

Coldness, sweatiness, flabbiness. Sourness of discharges and stools. Large and hard abdomen. Constipation. Crave indigestible things, e.g. chalk, cardboard, coal. Tapeworms and roundworms. Digestive upsets from milk. Diarrhoea sour, green, and watery. Coldness of affected parts. Cold, damp feet. Glandular problems. Big appetite. ***Modalities:*** *<< milk. < cold raw air; exertion.* ***Useful for:*** Overweight, sluggish hedgehogs, esp. babies. Bone disorders. Conjunctivitis. Umbilical hernia. Urinary infections. ***Instructions for Use:*** Don't give Sulphur after Calc carb.

Calendula

Haemorrhage. Cuts and lacerated wounds. Pain out of proportion to injury. ***Useful for:*** A great healer of wounds. Antiseptic, antibacterial, antiviral, and antiprotozoan. Cleansing. Quickly stops wounds bleeding. ***Instructions for Use:*** Mainly used externally. Don't use on deep, dirty, puncture wounds since surface may heal too fast, leaving dirt trapped inside – use Hypericum instead.

Cannabis indica

Out of touch with reality. Exaggerated mental symptoms. Urinary problems; straining, urine passed drop by drop. ***Useful for:*** Babies and juveniles that are *hyperactive*. Actually very sick, they seem unaware of this and will wear themselves out and finally collapse if not treated.

Cantharis

Painful urination. Difficult urination; dribbling of urine. Frequent urge to urinate. Amorous. Blisters, burns. Violent and acute inflammation. Very thirsty. ***Modalities:*** *< drinking.* ***Useful for:*** Main remedy for cystitis, esp. when painful. Very useful for burns, scalds, and sunburn, when given internally and applied externally. Stops blistering.

Carbo veg

Blueness of mucous membranes, dark haemorrhages. Septic conditions. Decomposition. Collapse. Weak, sick, and exhausted. Ill effects of excessively rich food. Sluggishness. ***Modalities:*** *> cool air, being fanned.* ***Useful for:*** Often revives a severely collapsed animal. Stopped breathing, or very weak, difficult breathing. Pneumonia. Flatulence. Abdomen filled with gas. Icy coldness. Poor circulation. Sloughing of skin, gangrene.

Causticum

Burns and scalds. Fright. Weakness of muscles, nerves. Anxiety (esp. in evenings). ***Modalities:*** *< dry cold winds. > cold drinks, warmth.* ***Useful for:*** Main remedy for burns, esp. deep burns. Will relieve the pain and shock of burns. Urinary problems, esp. incontinence or retention. Paralysis from muscle weakness or nerve damage.

Chamomilla

Teething problems. Irritable, restless, cannot tolerate pain. Hot, thirsty. Redness. Want many things, but refuse them when offered. Colic. Sour, grass-green stools that contain bits of flesh and smell like bad eggs. Fretful and irritable. **Modalities:** *< anger; night; drugs. > being carried/petted.* **Useful for:** Teething and colic. Esp. useful for infants.

China

Ill effects caused by loss of vital fluids. Profuse discharges. Anaemia. Oversensitive. Haemorrhage. **Useful for:** Animals weakened by loss of fluids, e.g. from bleeding, diarrhoea, or when dehydrated. Bloating and flatulence.

Cina

Very touchy and irritable. Don't like to be looked at. Worms. **Modalities:** *< touch.* **Useful for:** Expelling worms; give in mother tincture or very low potency.

Conium mac

Debility and weakness, effects of overexertion, injury, sexual excess. Trembling. **Useful for:** Old males, esp. those with strong sexual drive. Can be useful for hedgehogs running in circles. Paralysis, loss of use of limbs.

Euphrasia

Watery eyes. Bland, watery, nasal discharges. **Modalities:** *< sunlight, warmth; wind; indoors. > open air.* **Useful for:** Main remedy for runny eyes, with profuse hot or acrid tears, whether from injury or infection. Sticky eyes. Conjunctivitis. Opacities of cornea after injury. Can be used in solution to bathe eyes. **Instructions for Use:** Only use water that is sterile for bathing eyes.

Ferrum phos

Initial stages of fever and inflammation. Discharges blood streaked. Excited. Anaemic. **Modalities**: *< night.* **Useful for:** Inflammations in early stages, esp. ears, digestive upsets. Stools of bloody water. Very good for anaemia. **Instructions for Use:** When treating anaemia, give in tissue salt form (i.e. 6x twice daily for two weeks) to restore haemoglobin levels to normal.

Gelsemium

Shock, ordeals, fear, and dread. Dullness, drowsiness. Slow onset of symptoms. Thirstlessness. Catarrh of mucous membranes. **Modalities:** *> urination. < heat.* **Useful for:** Congestive complaints, catarrh, coryza, with heaviness, slowness, and dullness. Effects of fright, shock. Before ordeals, e.g. going to vet. Polyuria. Tremors, twitchings.

Graphites

Skin problems, thick and crusty, cracks and fissures. Constipation. Tape worms. **Modalities**: *< cold; night.* **Useful for:** Very useful skin remedy where dry and cracked, or oozing glutinous moisture.

Hepar sulph

Oversensitive to all impressions. Very irritable, quarrelsome. Suppuration. Foul discharges. Wounds fester. **Modalities**: *> heat, warm covers; damp air. < cold, uncovering; touch, lying on painful part.* **Useful for:** Very good for infected wounds or abscesses (will relieve pain and help the body to overcome the infection). Respiratory problems with weakness and rattling in chest.

Hypericum

Shock. Concussion of brain or spine, coccyx and tail. Damage to nerves and sentient tissue. Puncture wounds, esp. bites. Nerve pains. **Modalities**: *< injury, jarring.* **Useful for:** Main remedy for injuries involving spine or nerve damage. Bites or deep puncture wounds, when used internally and externally. Prevents infection developing and treats it if already present. Anti-tetanus. Will stop hedgehogs biting feet, e.g. due to pain or injury. **Instructions for Use:** Give after amputations because it stops pain. A good mixture for applying to wounds is Hypercal (equal parts Hypericum and Calendula).

Ignatia

Grief. Shock, esp. emotional or from fright. Chilly. Oversensitive, nervous. Spasms, twitchings. **Modalities**: *> warmth.* **Useful for:** Main use is for orphans or hedgehogs who are affected by loss. Can also be used in physical complaints where the animal has become stressed due to loss, shock, or fright. Colic. Loss of appetite.

Lachesis

Puncture wounds. Septicaemia. Symptoms move from left side to right side. Blueness of affected parts. **Modalities**:

< *after sleep; morning; heat, sun; slight touch or pressure; suppressed discharges.* > *open air; unsuppressed discharges; cold drinks.* **Useful for:** Hedgehogs that are very toxic, e.g. from poisoning or septicaemia. Good for heart and circulatory problems. Flesh wounds that have ulcerated.

Ledum

Chilly; affected parts cold yet are improved by cold bathing and made worse by warmth. Purpleness and puffiness of affected parts. Puncture wounds. Insect bites and stings. **Useful for:** Give initially after bites or other puncture wounds to prevent infection and tetanus (if already infected, use Hypericum). Eye injuries. Crusty eruptions round nose and mouth. Bronchitis, emphysema.

Lycopodium

Digestive problems. Full of gas. Flatulence. Liver problems. Cross and irritable. Symptoms move from right to left side. Likes sweet things. Eats only a little at once, as easily full up, or ravenously hungry. **Modalities:** < *cold; 4 to 8pm; on awakening.* > *warmth, warm drinks.* **Useful for:** All kinds of digestive upsets, especially where there is wind and aggravation from vegetables and milk. Hepatitis. Urinary problems, red sand in urine, calculi.

Mercurius sol

Glandular swelling, suppuration. Discharges offensive and green or greenish yellow. Easily chilled or overheated. Saliva excessive. Patients will be hurried, nervous, and inclined to bite when Merc sol is needed. Restless, want to escape. **Modalities:** < *night; when heated; drafts.* > *moderate temperature.* **Useful for:** Digestive upsets, especially when stools are green, slimy, and bloody. Jaundice.

Nux vomica

Angry and impatient, oversensitive to any stress. Gastric upsets, vomiting. Colic. **Modalities:** < *cold; open air; drugs; suppression of discharges; pressure.* > *unsuppressed discharges; rest.* **Useful for:** Diarrhoea. Ill effects of drugs. Blood in stools or urine. Thin quick, active, nervous hedgehogs. Constipation alternating with diarrhoea. Irritable bladder. Legs numb, paralysis; drags feet. Cough with bloody expectoration. Loss of appetite.

Phosphorus

Respiratory problems. Haemorrhage of bright red blood. Very impressionable. Increased sexual desire. Craves cold drinks. **Modalities:** < *cold; left side; slight stresses.* > *eating; sleep.* **Useful for:** Mainly on nerves, stomach, and bowels, everything that upsets these. Good for fearful, friendly hogs sensitive to noise. Pneumonia, esp. of left lower lung. Bronchitis. Burns. Ill effects of anaesthetics. Effects of fluid loss. Copious, debilitating diarrhoea.

Pulsatilla

Ill effects of suppressed discharges or excessively rich food. Changeability. Thirstlessness. Bland yellow discharges. Capriciousness. Hedgehog likes attention. Is easily upset. Craves foods which aggravate it. Chilliness. **Modalities:** < *warmth, warm room; evening; eating; puberty; getting wet, esp. feet; on beginning to move.* > *fresh air; cold.* **Useful for:** Gastric problems, esp. from food that is too rich or fatty. Catarrhal conditions. Likely to be useful for juveniles. Respiratory problems.

Rhus tox

Sprains, strains. Restlessness from pains. Stiffness that gets better with warmth. Vesicular eruptions. Anxious, despondent. **Modalities:** < *damp, exposure to wet cold weather; on beginning to move.* > *continued motion.* **Useful for:** Any sprain injuries. Chills from getting cold and wet.

Ruta grav

Injuries to fibrous tissue. Bruised bones. Sprains and dislocations. Lameness. Dissatisfied. Heaviness and weariness. **Modalities:** < *motion; cold; damp.* **Useful for:** Injuries to cartilage, tendons, and ligaments.

Silica

Ill effects of loss of vital fluids. Prostration. Every injury festers. Effects of poor nutrition. Abscesses and fistula. Foreign bodies. Fungal infections. Wounds slow to heal. Chilly. Constipation; hard to pass even soft stools. Abdomen distended, hard. Urinary problems. Produces much pus. Seeks warmth. Chronic catarrh. Creamy pink discharges. **Modalities:** < *cold; drafts; damp.* > *warmth, warm covers.* **Useful for:** Digestive upsets and respiratory problems. Expelling foreign bodies, e.g. splinters.

Sulphur

Hot, dirty, and smelly. Irritable. Skin problems. Parasites. Thirsty. Itchy. Diarrhoea and colic in infants. Pneumonia and other respiratory problems. Falling prickles and hair. **Modalities**: *< heat; suppressed discharges; bathing; overexertion; atmospheric changes; ill effects of drugs > open air; cool weather.* **Useful for**: *Main remedy for clearing ill effects of drugs or poisons.* Relieves itching. Helps improve resistance to parasites, both internal and external. Where the remedy picture is not clear, Sulphur "focuses" it, making it easier for you to spot the right remedy (which is also likely to work better after the Sulphur). Very good for coughs due to lung worm. Thin hedgehogs who eat a lot.

Symphytum

Fractures. Injury from blunt instruments. Injuries to face and eyes. **Useful for**: Known as knit bone, it does just that; any broken bones will heal much faster when this is given. Also relieves pain from fractures. Injury to cartilage and periosteum, and old injuries that have not healed. Relieves irritation from stump after amputation.

Tarentula hispanica

Nervous, hurried, erratic, changeable. Trembling, twitching. **Modalities**: *< touch; cold; noise; damp. > open air; music.* **Useful for**: Hyperactive babies and juveniles who are restless and sensitive to noise and touch. Will be soothed by gentle music. Hyperactivity is very serious and is usually followed by collapse if not treated.

Thuja

Hurried, twitchy, nervous, esp. of strangers. Warts. Fungal growths. Digestive disturbances with rumbling, gurgling. Urinary problems. Moist skin eruptions. Flaky skin. **Modalities**: *< cold and/or damp. Symptoms < on left side. < 3am & 3pm. > warmth.* **Useful for**: Main remedy for warts, fungal infections, e.g. ringworm. Antibacterial.

Urtica urens

Burns and scalds. Diminished secretion of milk. Uric acid toxaemia. **Useful for**: Applied in solution to burns.

NOSODES

Remedies made from disease pathogens (e.g. bacteria) or from products of disease (e.g. pus). They act very powerfully and deeply, so use with caution. You can obtain them from a homeopath/homeopathic pharmacy.

You can use a nosode in four ways. 1) According to the presenting symptoms, as with other remedies. 2) Treat the particular condition from which it is made. 3) As a prophylactic against the disease from which it is made. 4) Where a case has not responded to well-indicated remedies; the appropriate nosode will unblock the case and subsequent remedies will work better.

NB: **Proteus, Salmonella, Staphylococcus,** and **Streptococcus** have only been used prophylactically or to treat the specific disease from which they were made.

Bacillinum: For ringworm; chronic catarrh conditions.

Candida albicans: Hedgehogs are prone to this and it is likely to multiply rapidly in a sick animal. Give when digestive problems fail to yield to other remedies.

E. coli: For diarrhoea, green stools, or when stools contain mucus or blood.

Psorinum: *For parasites and skin complaints. Dirty, scabby skin eruptions break out in folds of skin. Very itchy made worse by heat of bed. Very chilly.* Hedgehogs will scratch until they bleed. Anxious and despondent. Foul discharges. Respiratory problems. Use when there is lack of reaction to other remedies. **Modalities**: *< cold; washing; open air; suppression of discharges.*

Pyrogen: For *septicaemia, abscesses, foul discharges, formation of pus.* Poisoning from gaseous substances. **Modalities**: *< cold; damp. > heat, hot bathing.*

Syphilinum: *Use when weakness and debility are out of proportion to symptoms. For ulceration, succession of abscesses. Green discharges.* Foul discharges. Snuffles; catarrh. When hedgehogs are antisocial or seem hopeless. **Modalities**: *<< night.*

Tuberculinum: *For irritable, sensitive, dissatisfied, changeable hedgehogs. Crave cold milk.* When symptoms change constantly or well-selected remedies fail to improve condition. For respiratory problems, such as pneumonia. Skin problems and ringworm. **Modalities**: *< cold; damp; change of weather; a warm stuffy room. > open air.*

Hedgehogs that are losing weight need worming. The safest wormer is fenbendazole. Open circles on the chart mean the product is not completely effective in that area. Always check droppings after treatment – if wormer has been effective dead worms will be shed.

The constituents in various milks are compared below. Feed tiny hogs with small teats made of Liquid Latex (from craft shops) fitted to a syringe.

SAFE WORM TREATMENTS FOR HEDGEHOGS

ANTHELMINTIC	INTESTINE			LUNGS		DOSE RATE
	Nematodes	Fluke	Tapeworm	Capillaria	Crenosoma	
Fenbendazole (Panacur,Hoechst)	●	●	●	●	○	Oral 110mg/500mg, 1 week interval - or divide over 5 days
Mebedazole (Telmin, Janssen)	●	●	○	●	●	Oral 50mg/500g, (1/2tab.) daily for 5 days *
Praziquantel (Droncit, Bayer)		●	●			Oral 12.5mg/500g, (1/2 tab.) x 2. 48 hrs inject s.c.0.1ml/500g *
Levamisole (Citarin, Bayer)	●			○	●	Inject s.c. 0.5ml/500g x 2 48 hrs. use 1.25% solution or less *

* Give half dose to hedgehogs under 500g. Treatment may need repeating 3-4 weeks later. WHH trials have found products containing Avermectins ineffective and unsafe for use in hedgehogs.

HEDGEHOG MILK COMPARISON CHART

MILK	WATER %	PROTEIN %	FAT %	SUGAR%	ASH %	NOTES
Hedgehog	79.4	6.5	9.68	1.89	2.06	High protein and fat with low sugar content
Esbilac liquid	85	4.5	6	3.5	1	
Goat	84.1	4	6	5	1	Add vitamins
Sheep	81.9	5.8	6.5	4.8	0.9	Add vitamins
Esbilac powdered	67	11.22	14.19	4.99	2.4	Do not switch from liquid to powder
Lamlac powdered	80	5	6	7	1	Powdered products can cause blockages in small orphans
Pig	84.6	6.3	4.8	3.4	0.9	Add vitamins
Whiskas liquid	83	4.2	3.7	0.4	0.9	Add vitamins
Skimmed Cows	90	3.6	0.8	4.6	0.8	Other products are better Add egg and vitamins
Cows	97.4	3.4	3.8	4.8	0.8	Cannot digest lactose and fat

If possible add 1/3 colostrum to milk for 41 days from birth. Fat and protein levels are important; water, egg or corn oil can be added to make substitute closer to hedgehog milk. (% are approx, compositions may vary.)

Hedgehog Resources

Equipment

Baby bottle sterilising solution and warmer (chemist)

Bulbs, coloured (electrical lighting supplier or specialists, such as Hygeia Manufacturing Ltd., Brook House, Avening, Glos GL8 8NS)

Bulbs, daylight simulation/Craft lights (lighting or craft shop)

Disinfectant, veterinary (from a vet or by mail from Millpledge Pharmaceuticals, Freepost, Retford, Notts DN22 9BR. Tel: 01777 705142/Fax: 860020)

Dressings, bandages, splints, absorbent pads & other veterinary supplies (by mail from Millpledge – see above for address).

Glucometers (by mail from Bayer Diagnostics – see Urine testing strips for address)

Heat lamps and pads (by mail from Southern Aviaries – see Incubators for address)

Incubators, thermostatically controlled (Brio Super Breeder available by mail from Southern Aviaries, Brook House, Tinkers Lane, Hadlow Down, Nr. Uckfield, East Sussex TN22 4EU. Tel: 01825 830283/830241)

Ionisers (health food shop, chemist)

Microscope and slides (by mail from Brunell Microscopes Ltd., Unit 8, Pickwick Workshops, Park Lane, Corsham, Wilts SN13 0HN. Tel: 01249 701601)

Stethoscope (chemist, veterinary supplier)

Ultraviolet (Woods) lamp (stationer, vet supplier)

Urine testing strips (chemist, vet supplier, or by mail from Bayer Diagnostics plc, Evans House, Hamilton Close, Houndsmill, Basingstoke, Hants RG21 6YE. Tel: 01256 29181)

Water jet, dental (Aqua Floss by mail from Ideal Home House, 9 Flag Business Exchange, Peterborough PE1 5TX. Tel: 01733 890158.)

Food & Supplements

Acidophilus (health food shop or by mail from Probiotics International Ltd., Stoke-sub-Hamdon, Somerset TA14 6QE Tel: 01935 822921. Ask for Protexin)

Charcoal (health food shop, chemist)

Colostrum, goat's (find your local goat breeder from The British Goat Society, 34-36 Fore St., Bovey Tracey, Newton Abbot, Devon TQ13 9AD. Tel: 01626 833168)

Colostrum, sheep's dried (by mail from Volac International Ltd., Volac House, Orwell, Royston, Herts SG8 5QX. Tel: 01223 208021)

Complan (chemist)

Eggs, organic free-range (find your local supplier from The Soil Association, 86-88 Colston St., Bristol BS1 5BB. Tel. 0117 9290661)

Eggs, quail eggs (supermarket, delicatessen)

Food, hedgehog (by mail from The British Hedgehog Preservation Society (see Contacts for address)

Electrolyte replacement – Dioralyte (chemist) and Lectade (vet)

Glucose powder (chemist)

Glycerine (chemist)

Insect food, dried or soft bill insectivorous bird food (Haith's Softbill Food by mail from John E. Haith, Park St., Cleethorpes, South Humberside DN35 7NF. Tel: 01472 357515/Fax: 242883)

Insects, live (live food suppliers or mealworms, waxworms, red earth worms by mail from The Mealworm Company Ltd., Unit 1, Universal Crescent, North Anston Trading Estate, Sheffield S31 7JJ. Tel: 01909 568953/4/Fax: 568666)

Kaolin (chemist)

Lactobacillus (health food shop or by mail from Probiotics – see Acidophilus for address)

Meat, organic (find your local supplier from The Soil Association – see Eggs for address)

Meat, convalescence food for syringe-feeding (Hill's Prescription Diet from vet)

Meat, tinned (Dene's Healthmeal from health food shop, pet shop)

Milk, goat's (goat breeder – see Colostrum – or health food shop)

Milk, sheep's (health food shop or by mail from Volac – see Colostrum, sheep for address)

Milk substitute. Esbilac by Pet Ag Inc. (by mail from Pat Murgatroyd, 43 Foxwood Lane, Acomb, York YO2 3LH. Tel: 01904 799161.

Paraffin, liquid (chemist)

Parsley and Watercress supplement (by mail from Dorwest Herbs, Shipton Gorge, Bridport, Dorset DT6 4LP. Tel: 01308 897272)

Seaweed supplements (health food shop or Kelp Seaweed Powder from Dorwest Herbs – see Parsley for address)

Slippery elm (chemist, health food shop)

Slug control (leaflet *On the slug's trail* from HDRA, Ryton Gardens, Ryton-on-Dunsmore, Coventry CV8 3LG. Tel: 01932 820958)

Tree Barks Powder (by mail from Dorwest – see Parsley for address)

Vitamin and Mineral supplement (Vetamin by mail from Millpledge – see Dressings for address). Abidec baby vitamin drops (chemist).

Remedies

Aromatherapy oils (health food shop)

Bach flower remedies (health food shop)

Crystals (New Age shops or by mail from Opie Gems, 57 East St., Ilminster, Somerset TA19 0AW. Tel: 01460 52346 and from Winfalcon's Healing Centre, 28-29 Ship St., Brighton BN1 1AD. Tel: 01273 739680 (office) or 728997)

Ear drops, Assissi (by mail from Assissi Ltd, Knutsford, Cheshire WA16 6HL)

Garlic juice (from Dorwest Herbs – see Parsley for address)

Herbs (by mail from Potters (Herbal Supplies) Ltd., Douglas Works, Leyland Mill Lane, Wigan, Lancs WN1 2SB. Tel: 01942 234761 and from Dorwest Herbs – see Parsley for address)

Homeopathic remedies (health food shop or chemist). For full range of remedies and potencies of the highest quality, buy direct from a homeopathic pharmacy. You can obtain remedies overnight (if urgent, say so when ordering) by post from the following:-

Helios Pharmacy, 97 Camden Road, Tunbridge Wells, Kent TN1 2QR.Tel: 01892 537254/ 53639/Fax: 546850.

Galen Homoeopathics, Lewell Mill, West Stafford, Dorchester, Dorset DT2 8AN. Tel: 01305 263996/Fax: 250792.

Ainsworths Homoeopathic Pharmacy, 36 New Cavendish St. London W1M 7LH. Tel: 0171 935 5330/Fax: 486 4313.

Nelsons Homeopathic Pharmacy, 73 Duke St., Grosvenor Square, London W1M 6BY. Tel: 0171 629 3118/495 2404 (mail order)

Goulds Homoeopathic Chemist, P.O. BOX 1019, 14 Crowndale Road, London NW1 1TH. 0171 388 4752/387 1888

Purple plates (New Age shops or by mail from Winfalcon's Healing Centre – see Crystals for address)

Contacts

The Welsh Hedgehog Hospital, Gwarffynnon, Llanddeiniol, Nr. Aberystwyth, Dyfed.SY23 5AR. Tel: 01974 241381/Fax: 241237. In 1993, a fire destroyed the Durrants' home and much of the hospital's records and reference material. The WHH exists solely on donations. Future plans include a larger building with extended laboratory facilities. Please help by making a donation or by sponsoring a hedgehog. TheWHH produces booklets on topics such as treatment, orphans and parasites, and holds an Open Day in August; at other times, visiting is by appointment only. If you need information, please write, enclosing an s.a.e.

Hedgehog Helpline, Kay Heaton-Jones, 5 Foreland Road, Whitchurch, Cardiff CF4 7AR. Tel: 01222 623985

The British Hedgehog Preservation Society, Knowbury House, Knowbury, Ludlow, Shropshire SY8 3LQ. Tel: 01584 890287

St Tiggywinkles, Wildlife Hospital Trust, Aston Road, Haddenham, Aylesbury, Bucks HP17 8AF. Tel: 01844 292292

RSPCA Wildlife Hospital, West Hatch, Taunton, Somerset TA3 5RT. Tel: 01823 480156. Is experienced in the use of homeopathy.

RSPCA. All calls to 0990 555999, you will then be rerouted to your local office for help. All correspondence to RSPCA Headquarters, Causeway, Horsham, West Sussex RH12 1HG.

The Born Free Foundation, Coldharbour, Dorking, Surrey RH5 6HA. Tel: 01306 712091/713320/713431/Fax: 713350

The British Wildlife Rehabilitation Council, c/o RSPCA or Kay Heaton-Jones (Hedgehog Helpline)

The British Association of Homoeopathic Veterinary Surgeons, Chinham House, Stanford-in-the-Vale, Oxon SN7 8NQ. Tel: 01367 710324.

The Society of Homoeopaths, 2 Artizan Road, Northampton NN1 4HU. Tel: 01604 21400

National Federation of Spiritual Healers, Church St., Sunbury on Thames, Middlesex TW16 6RG. Tel: 01932 783163/0891 616080.

The Harry Edwards Spiritual Healing Sanctuary, Burrows Lea, Shere, Guildford, Surrey GU5 9QG. Tel: 01483 202054.

Bibliography

Black's Veterinary Dictionary. A&C Black

Boericke, William. *Materia Medica with Repertory*. B. Jain 1983

Bomford, Liz. *The Secret Life of the Hedgehog*. Hamlyn 1979

Brennan, Barbara Ann. *Hands of Light*. Bantam Books 1987

Burton, Maurice. *The Hedgehog*. Corgi 1969

Castro, M. *The Complete Homeopathy Handbook*. Papermac 1991

Chapman, B.M. *Homeopathic Treatment for Birds*. C.W. Daniel 1991

Davis, Patricia. *A-Z of Aromatherapy*. C.W. Daniel 1988

Day, Christopher. *The Homoeopathic Treatment of Small Animals*. C.W. Daniel 1984

Gimbel, Theo. *The Book of Colour Healing*. Gaia Books 1994

Gurudas. *Gem Elixirs and Vibrational Healing*. Cassandra Press 1985

Harland, M. & Finn, G. *The Barefoot Homoeopath*. Hyden Ho 1991

Harper, Peter. *The Natural Garden Book*. Gaia Books 1994

Holbeche, Soozi. *The Power of Gems and Crystals*. Piatkus 1989

Levi, Juliette de Bairacli. *The Complete Herbal Handbook for Farm and Stable*. Faber 1952. *The Complete Herbal Handbook for the Dog and Cat*. Faber 1955

Lovelock, James. *Gaia, The Practical Science of Planetary Medicine*. Gaia Books 1991

MAFF/ADAS *Manual of Veterinary Investigation Laboratory Techniques*. HMSO 1978

McKibben, Bill. *End of Nature*. Penguin 1990

Morris, Pat. *Hedgehogs*.Whittet Books 1983

Morris, Pat. *The Hedgehog*. Shire 1988

Murphy, Robin. *Homeopathic Medical Repertory*. Hahnemann Academy of N. America 1993

Phatak, Dr. S.R. *Materia Medica of Homoeopathic Medicines*. B. Jain 1977

Price, S. *Aromatherapy for Common Ailments*. Gaia Books 1991

Reeve, Nigel. *Hedgehogs*. T. & A.D. Poyser 1994

Scheffer, Mechthild. *Bach Flower Therapy*. Thorsons 1990

Shine, Betty. *Mind Magic*. Corgi Press 1991

Stocker, Les. *The Complete Hedgehog*. Chatto & Windus 1987

Thienpont, D., Rochette, F., & Vanparijs, O.F.J. *Diagnosing Helminthiasis by Coprological Examination*. Janssen Research Foundation 1979

Walker, Dr.A. *The Definitive Book of Colour Healing*. Headquarters Publishing Co. 1991

Index

More titles from Gaia Books

Folk Remedies for Common Ailments
Anne McIntyre
£8.99
ISBN 1 85675 086 8
Successful and reliable cures for nearly
300 conditions. An invaluable resource
for self help, prevention and first aid
from your kitchen, bathroom
or hedgerow.

Homeopathy for Common Ailments
Robin Hayfield
£7.99
ISBN 1 85675 021 3
Safe, natural remedies for physical and
emotional problems, from croup to
chicken pox, anxiety to earache,
bites, stings and hayfever. Ideal for
children's treatments.

The Natural Garden Book
Peter Harper, Jeremy Light and Chris Madsen
£18.99 Hardback
ISBN 1 85675 085 X
£14.99 Paperback
ISBN 185675 056 6
This book is a fresh, practical and inspiring
guide to creating a productive, healthy garden.
Full of information on natural
gardening techniques.

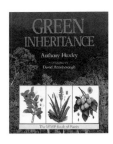

Green Inheritance
The WWF Book of Plants
Anthony Huxley
Foreword by David Attenborough
£10.99
ISBN 1 85675 000 0
Plants feed the world and are used
everywhere in the treatment of sickness.
They are the guardians of our survival.
The more we know about them, the
better are their chances as well as our own.
"Brilliantly informative" Sunday Times

The Gaia Rainforest Theatre
Designed by Rick Miller
£12.50
ISBN 1 85675 080 9
This sturdy pop-up theatre contains
19 push-out animal, plant and human
rainforest dwellers for endless
imaginative play, plus three
rainforest playscripts.

For a catalogue of titles published by Gaia Books, write or telephone
Gaia Books, 20 High Street, Stroud, Gloucestershire, GL5 1AS. Tel 01453 752985, Fax 01453 752987